Release Your Stress

Susan Balfour

HELP YOURSELF

British Library Cataloguing in Publication Data
A record for this book is available from the British Library

ISBN 0 340 78588 8

Typeset by Avon Dataset Ltd, Bidford-on-Avon, Warks

Printed and bound in Great Britain by
The Guernsey Press Co. Ltd, Channel Isles

Hodder & Stoughton
A Division of Hodder Headline Ltd
338 Euston Road
London NW1 3BH

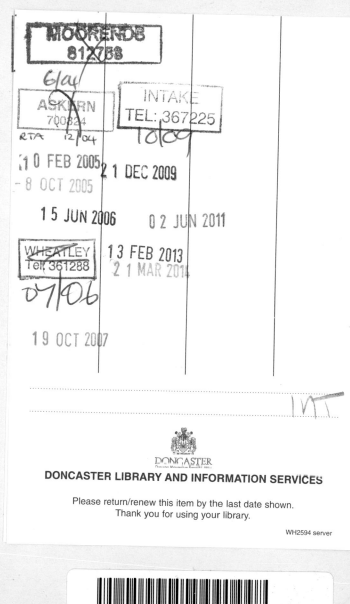

DONCASTER

DONCASTER LIBRARY AND INFORMATION SERVICES

Please return/renew this item by the last date shown.
Thank you for using your library.

WH2594 server

I dedicate this book to my loving parents,
who embodied so many of the positive attitudes
and values that I am expounding in these pages,
and who gave me strong foundations.

Contents

Acknowledgments

First, I want to thank all my friends for understanding that I could not talk to them, or go out to play, for the past six months, while I have been cloistered away writing this book between all other work commitments. But let me issue a warning: watch out now that I have finished! Great thanks are due to my daughter, Zara, for her support in helping with some of the typing, and particularly in being my very own technical support team – not to mention her insightful comments, which are always astute. Thanks to Paul Zabihi for reading some of the manuscript, and pausing to discuss ideas, when he really had no time! I should like to express my gratitude to my literary agent, Charlotte Howard, for her support and helpful suggestions.

As always, I am deeply indebted to Barbara Somers and the late Ian Gordon-Brown for their wonderful training in Transpersonal Psychology and for their outstanding example of 'walking the talk'. They unselfishly gave of themselves to thousands over the years, and much inspirational work is flowing into the world as a result of their wisdom and generosity of spirit. Barbara and Ian have a permanent place in my heart. As does Amber Lloyd, the indefatigable founder of Relaxation for Living, whose work has also helped and supported so very many people, over many years, suffering from tension, stress, panic attacks, hyperventilation and other symptoms of the stress syndrome. I am greatly appreciative of the knowledge and skills she taught me – most of which are included in this book – and of her support and encouragement in my work. I thank and acknowledge all those who have gone before, whose work and expertise have informed me; we all stand on the shoulders of others.

I thank my publisher, Judith Longman at Hodder & Stoughton, for her understanding of the process, her delightful attitude and her helpful thoughts and suggestions – so gently given and therefore so easy to receive. With great appreciation I thank John Clifton, who was always available to listen, and whose encouragement and receptivity to my writings helped more than he can know. Many thanks and gratitude also to Charles Edwards for his constant supportive interest, uplifting humour and wise comments. Two other dear friends at the end of the telephone line, whose supportive presence in my life means so much, are Susie Trotter-Landry and Jonathan Stedall - just thank you for being who you are; you are both always in my heart.

Introduction

In today's world we are becoming overwhelmed and overloaded by the very inventions that were supposed to enhance our quality of life; by the myriad of wonders we have created for ourselves. We now have so many choices, possibilities, optional extras and adornments to the basic processes of living, that, far from providing the promised freedoms and utopias, they are tending to weigh us down and clutter us up, often causing more problems than they solve and increasing the stress of life at every level.

Many books have been written on the subject of stress over the past decade or so; some of which have been heavy, academic and loaded with medical jargon, while others have attempted a lighter, sometimes rather superficial, approach. I believe, however, that a new kind of book is needed that views stress from a slightly different perspective; one that incorporates the old knowledge, but also looks at the subject with fresh eyes. We have entered a new age, a new century. The world moves on so rapidly and our approach to stress needs to move on also. We have different expectations in today's world, and different needs from our relatively recent past for our sense of wellbeing and contentment. Our awareness of ourselves, our fellow human beings and the planet we inhabit (not to mention the universe!), is changing almost daily due to the rapid advances in psychology, medicine, science and information technology, all of which tend to throw up new problems with which to grapple – alongside the benefits. In many ways, the goal posts have moved radically in the last few years – thus, I believe we must look at stress in terms of the new context in which we are living today.

Previously stress was seen as a phenomenon that only happened to certain people in certain extreme situations. Now we have to recognise that stress is an integral part of the current culture of humankind and it affects all of us in one way or another. Stress is impacting as never before, and creates much discomfort and unease for almost everyone on the planet. We can no longer ignore the evidence that we are creating an environment that is none too 'human-being-friendly', but equally, we cannot go backwards or easily undo what is already created. Therefore, we need to find new approaches and new strategies for living alongside the stresses of the modern world.

The new kind of stress book has to combine the necessary medical information (the physiological facts about the effects of stress on our bodily systems) with a contemporary 'take' on today's society, an analysis of what is happening to humankind at this point in the twenty-first century, which is very different from anything that has gone before. And a further dimension is needed: an inspiring and creative vision for the future – for how it could be, for how we *could* make it. But in order to create a better future, it is imperative that we are not bogged down or weakened by too much stress in current living; we need strategies that release us to be creative and enjoy our lives.

Often the only way to solve problems is to change the way you look at them and this is why I am writing another book on stress: to take a fresh, contemporary look at the dilemmas facing us right now, at this point in our history. In these pages I shall put before you some alternative ways of approaching and thinking about life and its constant challenges. I shall bring together the best solutions from the ancient wisdom teachings, translated into useful concepts and procedures for current living, as well as new perspectives on the best modern ideas. I shall endeavour to inspire you towards greater fulfilment, both now and in you

For, contrary to what many of us may
dilemmas of the complicated lifestyles we en
be resolved very easily, so that we can 'get bac
as possible; and they definitely won't be taken c
else! Therefore, we need to find new ways to deal w
and pressures that are the inevitable result of our mul   .ves,
overloaded by endless media, too much information   .cessant
communication, more choice than we can comfortably handle,
intense commercial pressure to have more possessions, be more
successful, more good-looking, more slender and smarter than our
peers. Not to mention the stress of daily threats to our wellbeing
from contaminated food, polluted atmosphere and powerful new
strains of bacteria, along with the potential environmental dangers
we have set up for ourselves, in terms of climate change and the
consequences of destroying our rainforests. I believe we need to
take a different perspective on it all; climb up, as it were, to the top
of the hill, to gain a new viewpoint.

In my view, we need to start reassessing how much of the 'stuff'
on our current agenda is truly helpful, life-enhancing and needed
on the journey into the new century, and those aspects that we
could safely relegate to the metaphorical trashcan or shredder. I
think a kind of millennial spring cleaning is needed, where we chuck
out all the unnecessary clutter and excess baggage we've been
accumulating – often unconsciously – both as individuals, on a
personal level, and as a species, on a global level.

That is what this book is about. I shall assist you in carrying out
an audit of your life on many levels to help you discover what is
weighing you down and holding you back, compared to that which
is truly helpful and supportive to your life goals. Every dwelling
place needs to be cleared out on a regular basis in order that the
occupants can function in a relaxed and effective fashion. If you are
constantly tripping over the clutter, or cannot find things buried
deep in the chaos, you become tense and stressed, angry and panicky.
Isn't this the state in which many of us find ourselves quite
frequently? And it is even more important to clear out the dwelling

oughts and feelings – our inner self- and address the
lutter which may no longer be useful to us. It is possible to
estep or offload much of our stress by changing the way we look
at it, or the way we go into action, and these are two major themes
I will expand upon throughout the book. I shall be offering
suggestions for new ways to tackle various different life areas and
new perspectives on old problems.

In the spring we feel the great uplift of renewal and rebirth, so
this is a great time to take a closer look at the stuff of our personal
life, perhaps to re-evaluate where we are heading. At this time of
year we often have a sense of new potential within ourselves longing
to be expressed, as well as new possibilities out there in the world
for us to action and initiate: this is exciting and energising. But if
we want to turn these possibilities into realities, we have to find
some spare room in our lives, and some new attitudes and energies.

Changing our habits isn't easy, but I think it can be helpful to see
that change is really development; and development is inevitable in
our lives. Just as a bud must develop into a flower and an acorn
must develop into an oak tree, so too must we develop and change
if we do not wish to stagnate, or regress. For nothing in Nature
stands still – we must develop or degenerate. Another way to see
this is as John F. Kennedy put it:

> 'You cannot become what you want to be by remaining what you
> are.'

I see life as a constant process of transformation, from one developmental stage to the next, and I think humankind currently stands
on the brink of a critical new stage in its development. I think
many of the stresses we face today – and many of the difficult world
events – are offering us a challenge to change and transform, to
rethink our values and objectives. I believe we are being challenged
to grow and mature as individuals, societies and nations. We are
being stressed into the realisation that we are interdependent and

that all actions ripple out to affect the whole of humanity: we have to take account of each other. We cannot act unilaterally, or selfishly any more, for we are so completely linked-up around the globe that there is always a knock-on effect – a domino effect that, one way or another, will eventually ripple back to impact upon the place from which it originated.

This thought may seem a little daunting, but it is a positive way to view much of what is happening in our world. If we do the right things, then the right things will rebound back at us. I truly believe that we have a serious challenge in front of us and that it can be life-enhancing if we approach it in the right spirit. Many people feel that much needs to change around the globe, but the place to start is with ourselves and our individual lives right here, right now. This book is offered as a starting point: as a combination of guide book, reference book, and supportive and inspirational companion on your developmental journey into recognising how to release your stress, and then perhaps help others do the same.

1

What's going on?

Stress has many causes, and stress can arise from any aspect of our lives, as well as being generated internally from our thoughts and feelings. We all have our own definitions as to what exactly constitutes stress and some people maintain that stress is good for us, as it keeps us focused and productive, while others would advise that we avoid stress at all costs if we want to be happy. As we proceed through this book I shall endeavour to address all the differing views on stress; I shall define stress in specific ways and in specific situations, and help you to understand more about how – and why – stress affects you physically, emotionally and mentally. But most importantly of all I shall present you with strategies for releasing yourself from its grip.

However we define stress, I believe there is a need to take a new look at this phenomenon, for there can be no doubt that we all feel increasingly stressed by much of our modern world, and in my view it is not going to get any better as we advance into the next few decades. In fact, I am convinced that the levels of stress will increase for quite a while. Or at least, the 'triggers' to stress will increase. It is therefore going to be up to each of us to ensure that we do not succumb, and that is what this book is about. We are going to need new strategies, to redesign our lives perhaps, to rethink many of our basic assumptions and to develop a new game-plan, a new philosophy even, for a new era.

This is already beginning to happen, in that many of us are looking for alternatives and new perspectives – in complementary medicine, in the rediscovery of ancient wisdoms, in going on retreats or taking holidays off the beaten track – there is almost a new consciousness beginning to unfold at the dawn of the new century.

This book is intended to be part of this very positive impulse to think for ourselves, to search for better ways to live, to do 'it' differently. You may have heard the saying: 'The future is another country; they do things differently there.' It is my wish, and my intention in this book, to provide a guide and a sort of map into the new country of the future, with my suggestions for the best ways to go – the least stressful route! After almost twenty years of helping people to live in a better relationship with the stresses of life, I have come to certain conclusions and developed my own ideas and strategies for getting through with the least strain and the most joy, and I want to share these with you. Each chapter will address an aspect of daily life, look at why we become stressed by it, or bogged down in it, and then suggest ways to release ourselves – by taking a different approach, by rethinking and finding new perspectives, or by finding new ways to apply the old truths. We have to be inventive and creative – this is what we were born to be – and the more we apply our creativity the more fulfilled we will feel, and the less stressed.

The stress of change

Part of the stress being experienced at any moment in history comes from the tension generated by change; by the old order of things having to give way to new ideas and practices. This of course happens on the large scale, globally, as well as in the smaller arena of our own personal lives. Stress is the adaptation, or adjustment, the mind and body have to make to any changing circumstances, whether they are physical, psychological or emotional. The more extreme the adjustment required, the more we experience stress and possibly distress. And part of the reason that the stresses and tensions are impacting more profoundly and widely today than ever before, is the increasing speed with which new innovations are overtaking the old, and the huge demand this makes on all of us to adapt rapidly and frequently. On top of this demand to adjust our thinking, our practices and sometimes our priorities, there is now an additional demand for everything to happen faster than ever before, and for each moment to be filled more completely than ever – we expect to cram more and more achievement into each day.

This puts enormous pressure on us and on our coping ability. Our mental, emotional and physical resources are being stretched unceasingly, even though we may not always realise it from day to day. We know in an abstract way that this is the case, but in my view we don't really give enough thought to just what is happening to us at this point in the twenty-first century, which means that we don't take enough counter-measures, and I shall be addressing this important aspect of counterbalancing our stressors throughout the book. It all tends to creep up on us in an accumulative manner, and we adjust without quite realising what a strain it is to be confronted with relentless demands to absorb and react to high-speed news, views and innovation all around the clock.

Whether we realise it or not, this pressure to keep up to date – to keep abreast of it all – is impacting profoundly on most of us, most of the time. I see the results constantly in my therapy practice: people suffering from exhaustion, burn-out, panic attacks, hypertension and a whole host of other symptoms.

I think many people would agree that there is a general unease about the fact that we don't seem to feel as good as we think we should. A lot of advertising slogans emphasise 'peace of mind' as one of their benefits, for peace of mind is a tad elusive in our current world: in fact, levels of anxiety, depression and mental ill-health are rising, even among children. Today's lifestyle is not exactly producing the freedoms and happiness that were implicitly promised by the new technologies and so-called labour-saving devices.

People who come to consult with me know they feel overloaded and overstretched, and somehow unfulfilled in important aspects of themselves. There also seems to be a widespread feeling among many that they can't control their agendas sufficiently so as to create more time for what they really want to do. These are issues we shall be addressing as we proceed through the book. I shall analyse why we feel as we do, then offer you ideas and strategies for counteracting a lot of the pressures, as well as suggesting ways to take more control of your agenda to free up time for yourself, and to bring about more positive changes.

A theme I hear constantly is that people have little energy and always seem to feel under pressure to keep on doing, but often they don't quite understand how and why this is their current scenario. They say they feel driven by the multitude of tasks always needing their attention and panicky at not finding the time to step back, take an overview and work out a way of changing the situation. My clients tell me there never seems to be enough time or space in their schedule to take time out for themselves, or not enough time to relax or daydream to restore their energy. This is important, because so-called daydreaming, or 'pottering about' time is essential for rebalancing ourselves and connecting into the right hemisphere of the brain, from which arises much of our creativity and best ideas. Also, total relaxation of body and mind is one of the most effective counterbalances to overloading and excessive demands; deep relaxation restores depleted energy at all levels, mentally and physically. It is a technique I teach to all my clients as an indispensable tool in their stress-release strategy, and I will teach it to you in Chapter 7.

We tend to adjust to new circumstances without realising what is happening because we are very adaptable beings. But we need to take stock from time to time; step back and try to look objectively at our situation and reassess if we are living in a way that is right for us. We can cope with extra demands and high pressure for a while – but not as a constant way of life. If you are continually being loaded up with more and more to adapt and adjust to, without sufficient resting time in between, there comes a point where you will just collapse and burn out from unrelenting demand.

Limited adaptation energy

Change of any kind – even pleasant change – is stressful because human beings actually have a limited amount of adaptive capacity; it is different for each of us, but if we are pushed beyond our individual limit we find it hard to cope. It is often difficult to admit to ourselves that we have limits, but the truth is that we do! We deny this fact at our peril: it may be a long time before it catches up with us, but eventually it will. The people most at risk from stress-related symptoms are those who never relax, never really switch off; those who are not willing to admit to themselves – or anyone else, for that matter – that they feel tired, or that for the time being they have reached their limit. It is not a question of being an under-achiever, it is a question of balance, and in my experience the most successful people have almost always developed ways of switching off. I shall address this more fully in Chapter 7, but for the moment let's stay with the subject of change.

It is interesting to note that demanding life changes often cluster at the same time – things like getting married, moving house, changing jobs, having a baby, bereavement, divorce, redundancy, retirement and so on. They superimpose themselves on all the other aspects of change in the world around us. And because we do not have unlimited adaptive resources, it is imperative that we take extra care of ourselves when we are dealing with a number of life changes. This fact is well documented in medical literature, but generally not sufficiently well explained to the lay public.

Below is a list of the most demanding life events you can experience, with a numerical value against each. According to research carried out in the 1970s by doctors Thomas Holmes and Richard Rahe of the University of Washington School of Medicine, and largely undisputed by subsequent research, a score of 150 based on events which have happened to you in the previous twelve-month period, would make your chances of developing an illness or health change roughly 50–50. If you were to score 300 points or over within the year, your chances of experiencing a health change rise to almost 90 per cent, for you have reached the danger zone as far as your body's adaptive capacity is concerned. Your body's resilience to combat disease or maintain homeostasis (constant state of internal systems) will be severely taxed. For good health and emotional happiness try not to rise above a score of 150 points in any one year. Obviously, it would be best to keep most years well below even that figure. If you have had a high score in life-change events one year, give yourself a break and keep things much the same as usual in the following twelve months, or at least attempt to avoid the high score changes. If that proves impossible, then make sure you have more rest than usual during the high score times to counteract the strain, and don't take on any unnecessary changes at that time. It is also important to ensure you are eating a good diet which supplies vital replenishment to your body's resources. In these ways you can help to strengthen the body's defences against illness and breakdown of health. (See Chapter 8 for advice on diet.)

Life Events Chart

Event	Value
Death of a spouse	100
Divorce	73
Marital separation	65
Jail term	63
Death of close family member	63
Personal injury or illness	53
Marriage	50
Fired from work	47
Marital reconciliation	45
Retirement	45
Change in family member's health	44

Pregnancy	40
Sexual difficulties	39
Addition to family	39
Business readjustment	39
Change in financial status	38
Death of a close friend	37
Change to different type of work	36
Change in number of marital arguments	35
Mortgage or loan over £100,000	31
Foreclosure of mortgage or loan	30
Change in work responsibilities	29
Son or daughter leaving home	29
Trouble with in-laws	29
Outstanding personal achievement	28
Spouse begins or stops work	26
Starting or finishing school	26
Change in living conditions	25
Revision of personal habits	24
Trouble with boss	23
Change in work hours, conditions	20
Change in residence	20
Change in schools	20
Change in recreational habits	19
Change in church activities	19
Change in social activities	18
Mortgage or loan under £100,000	17
Change in sleeping habits	16
Change in number of family gatherings	15
Change in eating habits	15
Vacation	13
Christmas season	12
Minor violation of the law	11

Our cognitive interpretations of these life events also play a significant part; for if something like a divorce is more of a relief than an agony, it will not take such a toll on your health, although the actual changes involved will still have an impact on your adaptive energy. Some events will be experienced more traumatically by certain individuals than others, and will therefore be more depleting of the body's resources; this factor was not taken sufficiently into account in the early research. Each life event does not affect each person in exactly the same way, and it has been discovered in more recent research that one's attitudes can protect one's body. I don't mean you should artificially force yourself to experience joy in the face of sad events, but where it is possible and appropriate, altering one's attitude can do much to release stress, or at least to mitigate against the more extreme effects. However serious your life circumstances, or however over-stretched you may feel, try to take regular time out for laughter – it is a real tonic. Laughing expels your breath and is followed by deep inhalation, which relaxes you. It distinctly elevates your mood, which has been found to raise the pain threshold as well as increasing the production of immunoglobulins, which help defend you against illness and infection. I shall be saying much more regarding attitudinal approaches in many of the following chapters.

Dr Hans Selye was one of the pioneer researchers into the stress syndrome and its effects in the 1930s and 40s, and this is explained fully in his book, *The Stress of Life* (McGraw-Hill, revised edition, 1976). Hans Selye made an enormous contribution through his dedicated work, but I fear that his findings are not as well understood today as they might be. Much of my work is based on his research and the development of his understanding by his colleagues and his students in the generations that came afterwards. I shall be alluding to his work throughout this book, as well as to other important specialists in the field of understanding stress. I shall attempt to translate the medical findings into lay terms, as well as into practical, useful everyday applications for releasing your stress.

In relation to our limited adaptive capacity, Dr Selye wrote, 'It is as though, at birth, each individual inherited a certain amount of adaptation energy, the magnitude of which is determined by his genetic background, his parents. He can draw upon this capital thriftily for a long but monotonously uneventful existence, or he can spend it lavishly in the course of a stressful, intense, but perhaps more colourful and exciting life. In any case, there is just so much of it, and he must budget accordingly.'

If you don't budget, but overspend your adaptation energy by having to adapt or adjust to too many changes in too short a space of time, you become bankrupt in terms of energy, with nothing left over for an emergency, or for unexpected change. So keep your eye on your energy bank, and try not to run it on permanent overdraft! Try to keep an ongoing energy 'savings account', so that you always have some reserves. In my opinion a great number of people nowadays are struggling to function in a state of permanent exhaustion, due to the high levels of demand we all face each day. Therefore, it is not surprising that we feel strained and not terribly happy much of the time. We must not neglect to pay in to our energy bank: we need to build our energy levels and other resources constantly, and we shall be looking at how to do this in many different ways throughout the book.

Change is also stressful because it can feel threatening: it threatens what we know and all that is familiar and predictable. So, however inevitable change may be, it takes its toll – today more than ever before.

Mitigating the effects of change

Given that change is not going to go away, or slow down, and that in all probability it will increase and intensify, it is going to become ever more necessary that we take this phenomenon seriously, and learn how to manage ourselves in relation to change.

So the first strategy in releasing yourself from stress must be to assess how much change you are currently coping with, or have been coping with in the recent past, whether or not you felt stressed by it. Managing change means mitigating the effects of change: that is, to minimise them as much as possible and/or compensate yourself during the changes and afterwards.

Some practical guidelines

* If you are faced with a number of inevitable, or unavoidable, changes try at least to stagger them, with resting periods in between each change, so that you do not overload yourself with too much to adapt to in a short period of time. Or break up each change into a number of stages, interspersed with time to rest and replenish yourself. If you cannot spread them out, but have to deal with many changes all at once, then plan some recovery time at the end of it all – time to do nothing very much while you adjust and acclimatise to the new situation or circumstances; time to recover your resources. Most importantly, do not just lurch from adjustment to adjustment without taking stock of what is happening to you, because it will exhaust your capabilities and absolutely everything will then seem more difficult than usual, for you will be running on empty, with no reserves.

* If you know a large number of changes are coming up in one area of your life, then make sure that you keep things as much the same as usual in other areas. For example: supposing you have received promotion at work, have just moved to new offices, acquired a new boss and new work colleagues, and are possibly having to learn a completely new computer system, then it would be inadvisable to move house (a very stressful event), attempt to learn a foreign language and start flying lessons at the same time! In other words, don't take on any extra, unnecessary, demanding activities.

* If, for example, you have recently been divorced (a big life change and adjustment), been forced to move out of your home and perhaps had a reduction in income, then that is quite enough for anyone to cope with at any one time. Do not take on any more change until you have had time to become accustomed to the new circumstances. In fact, the most stressful change in anyone's life is the loss of an important relationship or bereavement: you will note these rate the highest scores on the Life Events Chart.

This change needs a significant amount of time for adjustment to be made, and should not be hurried, or denied. You can probably understand how this kind of change of life circumstances depletes a person's resources, both emotionally and mentally, and how those stresses take their toll on the physical body. A person in this situation needs to be protected against any more stress, or change, and must give themselves permission not to take on too much until they feel stronger. All loss has a major impact on our normal coping ability, and this applies equally to loss of any part of our body, perhaps through surgery or accident, or to loss of usual use in certain limbs, as with paralysis, or disability like RSI (repetitive strain injury) or severe arthritis. All these things change your relationship with the world around you. Time is the greatest healer here and I would always advise, 'Just take your own time to adjust: don't push yourself, or allow yourself to be pushed by others.'

A client of mine has recently split up with her long-term boyfriend, and because she was living with him in his flat, she has had to move out. She is currently dividing her time staying with two different friends who have offered help, but who live on opposite sides of London, so she is spread between two different homes, with some of her things in each place. This is all very taxing to her emotional energy. She has lost her emotional partner and her home all at the same time, and has no secure base from which to operate. She also has no territory to call her own and it is affecting her performance at work. She has had a number of run-ins with her boss for forgetting important tasks and she has begun to talk about changing her job. I am trying to dissuade her from this, for she will destabilise herself even further. She does not recognise the stress she is under and simply wants to get away from what she perceives as 'hassle', but another major change in an important area of her life will weaken her at this point – it will not improve matters. She needs to keep as much as possible the same as usual while she adjusts to her new status. In a few months' time, when she has found a permanent home, she could start the search for a new job, but right now it would just add to the stress and strain to take on more change. I can only hope she will listen to my advice. But this is a good illustration of how intense life events can affect our capacity to cope in other areas.

- Another life change frequently experienced, but often under-estimated, is leaving school and going to university. Suddenly you are having to cope with completely organising your timetable alone: shopping for food and feeding yourself adequately on a small budget, making sure you have clean clothes and clean surroundings. You are responsible for lots of tasks that were probably taken care of by someone else before – usually your mother – on top of an extra intellectual workload. Not to mention the adjustment to new house-mates or fellow students in halls. A huge change of circumstances, usually not sufficiently acknowledged or prepared for. No wonder many undergraduates become depressed. Actually, they are probably not truly, clinically depressed, they are buckling under too much demand for change all at once; it is exhausting their resources.

- Similarly, children starting school for the first time are facing enormous adjustments, which will be taxing to their adaptation energy and which need to be taken into consideration when planning the rest of their timetable. The change of leaving the safe and relatively peaceful environment of home, to be con-fronted with scores of other children, new surroundings, new adults to relate to, on top of the strain of starting structured learning programmes, is all incredibly demanding and often not sufficiently understood by parents. It is little wonder that they are often crabby and bad-tempered when they come out of school! I always found one of the best ways to counteract the irritability was to make sure I met my daughter with something to eat, so as to raise her blood sugar level – a sticky bun or a sandwich or even some biscuits – which would supply instant sugar and cheer her up till she got home and could eat some better quality food. We are all irritable when our blood sugar is low. Try to be patient with them if they are difficult – they are just overloaded and need to get home to a protected, safe, quiet space, where they can coast for a while. Equally, make sure that your child is not overloaded with extra changes outside of school time, like ballet or music lessons, until they have adjusted. If possible, avoid dragging them round the supermarket after school, for that kind of environment provides too much sensory input for a tired child, usually causing them to go into a hyperactive state, which frays everybody's nerves and ends in arguments and tears. Protect and cosset them a little more than usual, and make sure they get sufficient sleep. Make bedtime a time of calm, with stories, songs or nursery rhymes, after a warm, soothing bath.

Children often contract frequent minor illnesses when they start school, which is due in part to mixing with a large number of other children, but is also due to the increased demand on their adaptive energy leaving less energy available for the body to combat invading organisms. This phenomenon is also seen in adults undergoing demanding or stressful changes. Teachers starting a new school year usually go through a phase of increased susceptibility to illness, and the same has also been noticed among medical students during the first months of their training, as well as others in new and demanding situations.

• Another mammoth change of lifestyle is experienced when a new baby is born, and often couples are not prepared for the toll this takes on their energies and adaptive capabilities. Many try to play down the change to their way of life – often because they don't feel ready to change anything – but in the first few months at least it is best to give yourselves plenty of 'floating' time with a minimum of demands in other areas. I think a great many new mothers become depressed due to exhaustion more than any other factor. They have high expectations of themselves, often expecting to be able to do everything they did before in addition to looking after their baby. But a baby's needs are many and unrelenting at first, and use up huge amounts of their mother's energy. Time is needed for adjustment to the new situation, not forgetting the internal changes and adjustments taking place in the new mother's hormone levels. Mothers must look after themselves as well as their newborn.

• Sometimes the death of an aged parent may coincide with our own retirement, or with children leaving home, or with one's partner being made redundant: another series of profound adjustments.

And we do adjust and adapt in time – the new circumstances become the 'norm' – we acclimatise, or habituate as psychologists like to say. In other words, the new has metamorphosed into the habitual, and demands less attention, therefore less energy.

Some changes we choose, and some are forced upon us, but just try to assess how much change you are dealing with when you are feeling particularly stressed and strained, and you may be surprised to realise how much change is, or has been, happening in your life. Also try to be aware of the changes that members of your family may be coping with, or in other close relationships: especially if you are experiencing difficulties with them, if people are more short-tempered than usual, or things blow up for no apparent reason. This could all be due to exhausted reserves of adaptation.

Just keep reminding yourself that too much change in too short a space of time will be severely debilitating, and may diminish your abilities in all areas of your life.

If most of the things you face each day feel more and more of a strain, even things that previously seemed relatively easy to cope with, this may indicate that you are handling too much change and exhausting your adaptation energy. So take mitigating, or compensating, action as suggested above – and below. You may even have to tell a 'white lie' or two, to evade any more demands on your over-stretched resources. This is simply good life management – and good sense!

2

Wisdom and truth: Vital resources

Hold on to what is valuable for you

It is not only the volume and velocity of change that is stressing us. Many people feel uneasy about the *kind* of changes that are happening, and our lack of control over them; this causes anxiety and emotional stress. For while a large number of today's changes may be exciting, interesting and 'good', a worrying level of what we are implementing is not good for us at all. Thus we are not only coping with rapid change, which can be overwhelming to our adaptation energy, but we also have to cope with the anxiety produced by all the 'wrong' things that are happening – the changes we perceive as bad for us, and for the planet. This is another load to carry. I am talking about things like genetically modified crops, cloning, polluted air, toxic waterways, gridlocked motorways, nuclear power plants and the transportation of nuclear waste, the devastation of the rainforests, climate change and much, much more that I shall come to later.

Is there anything we can do? Yes, I think there is, and I think it will have an influence eventually, firstly for our personal lives and then gradually for the whole planet.

I believe that the next most important step in our strategy to minimise and compensate for the strain and intensity of our changing world, is to ensure that we consciously retain, and regularly focus on, all the wisdom that has been accumulated through the ages. Those wise directives that instruct us in ways of living and behaving that have been passed down through the generations, and which are being squeezed off the current Agenda. There is a very relevant saying I heard a while ago, which is:

> *'Where is the Wisdom we have lost in knowledge, and where is the Knowledge we have lost in information?'*

It is tremendously important, in my view, both at a personal level and for humanity as a whole, that we don't lose sight of those eternal truths that do not change with changing fashions or new ideas, that do not go out of date, and which can give us a sense of stability, certainty and continuity in the face of change. These profound truths and wisdom have supported, sustained and inspired humankind through many changing scenarios. We must not forget what we know. If we lose our connection to truth, we will go further and further astray. In many ways you could say that all the answers we need are already with us, we just have to remind ourselves, search them out and apply them appropriately. This is one of the themes I shall be returning to again and again throughout the book. I shall search out the ancient wisdom teachings about different aspects of life and present them to you with suggestions about how to apply them in current living, in order to release your stress. But I would also encourage you to work on doing the same: to discover, or remember, the wisdom or truths that make sense to you.

They may come from a spiritual or religious belief system, a philosophical viewpoint or the wise traditions that have been passed down through the ages in each culture. They are the cornerstones of civilised life, and can act as touchstones when we feel overwhelmed or bewildered by all the demands of today's changing world that clamour for our attention. We need these guiding principles for our total wellbeing – that is, for the wellbeing of our soul and spirit, as well as our hearts and minds. If we return to these messages of truth and wisdom regularly throughout our day, we will know how to respond, what is best practice or the right basis for our approach to almost everything. They provide a calming point of certainty within the rapidly shifting, superficial values of our contemporary culture.

The test of a truth is that it can be applied at any time, in any situation, and so can transcend opinion or prejudice, and can speak to each and every human being regardless of race or creed; a truth always resonates as being true, and it provides an extra dimension – opens up the vista – in any situation.

Take some time out to reflect on this. What is your bottom line? What are your core values? Which are your own truths and guiding principles?

How to work with this in a practical way

I suggest that you create a list of all the most important truths that you use to support you in living your life, or those that you would like to implement more often. It may take you a while to bring these things up into consciousness, but if you give it the time and the serious consideration it deserves, you will find this mental exercise enormously rewarding and uplifting. Carry the list of truths around with you, to refer to when you feel blown off course – unpeaceful, stressed – to reassure you, and to remind you where the firm ground lies. Also pin up copies of your list somewhere in your home and workplace, even in your car (perhaps especially in your car!) so that you are constantly in touch with these foundation stones of life.

One example that comes to mind is the truth about the power of love; I don't think anyone would deny the power of love. This truth has been recognised and expressed in different ways throughout all recorded ages. A beautiful example being the twentieth-century song asserting that 'Love Changes Everything'. Call this to mind whenever you are in a difficult situation, or having problems with someone, and see if it changes the way you are looking at things. **Love Changes Everything**. Write it down, carry it around with you.

Set that beside the declaration of the thirteenth-century physician Paracelsus who is reported to have said:

> *'Love is the highest level of medicine.'*

This is an extraordinary statement that certainly deserves thinking about. It indicates the enormous power of love – the power to heal. I believe this to be so.

In the Bible, Christ is reported to have said:

> *'Love one another.'*

Buddha said:

> *'Let a man overcome anger by love.'*

Buddha also stated:

> *'Hatred is never conquered by hatred at any time; hatred is conquered by love.'*

I am sure each of you reading this will have your own favourite sayings about the power of love. It may be a line from a poem or a quote from Shakespeare, such as, 'Love is not love which alters when it alteration finds, or bends with the remover to remove. Oh no! It is an ever-fixed mark that looks on tempest and is never shaken.' Of course, it is not easy to love everyone, but just start out by trying to like people a bit more; look for the things that are likeable in another person or in a difficult situation.

An example of how to apply this truth: I used to lecture frequently to doctors and other health professionals, and also in the business community, and the way I developed my confidence and overcame my nervousness was to decide to love my audience. Instead of seeing my audience as a group of critics, ready to fault me at every turn, I took the attitude that I really wanted to give something to the people assembled in front of me, and that they really wanted to hear what I had to offer. So, with a feeling of warmth and love, and enthusiasm for what I was doing, I turned my thoughts outwards towards the people I was speaking to, and away from myself. I chose my inner attitude; I chose to love everybody and, of course, the result was very positive. There was actually no reason not to love, for I didn't know them, and so why feel frightened of them? Why not decide they were lovable? It all starts with us, after all; we are responsible for the attitudes with which we approach the outer world and each other. When we choose to love, it really does change everything.

So whenever you are experiencing difficulties with someone, make the decision to love them: feel love for them. See them not as a giant enemy, but as a fallible and flawed human being trying their best to cope – loaded down, as we all are, with their problems and worries. Deciding to love them will change the way you deal with them.

His Holiness the Dalai Lama says, in *The Little Book of Wisdom* (published by Rider),

> *'Practice love. To do so in all situations will take time, but you should not lose courage. If we wish happiness for mankind, love is the only way.'*

Another way of applying this truth is to make a decision to try to understand. Trying to understand another will always change the way you relate to them. Try to put yourself in their shoes. When we truly understand we develop compassion, and compassion produces love.

In the same little book (which I suggest you go out and buy) the Dalai Lama also says:

> *'Inner tranquility comes from the development of love and compassion.'*

This is an example of how an eternal truth can help you to find the solution or way through something difficult or stressful. It changes the perspective. It expands your viewpoint, enabling you to look at the situation or relationship from another level – the level of eternal truth. This level will give you all the answers, or clues, you need for coping with life and releasing your stress.

'What is Truth?' you may ask. The great spiritual book the *Bhagavad-Gita* maintains:

> *'Truth is that which is not born and does not die.'*

In other words, truth is timeless – it always has been, it always will be, and it is never changing.

Find your own eternal truths and pieces of recorded wisdom and say them to yourself regularly in your mind and in your heart – referring to your list to remind you – and most importantly, find ways to apply them in your life by letting them influence your behaviour. Affirm whatever the message means to you by repeating it to yourself many times a day – especially if you feel wound up, or stressed and upset. Words have a great power to influence our inner state.

Saying the right words can have a profound effect on how you think and how you feel, strengthening you inwardly; the more you repeat them the more they will have a positive influence on you. Repetition enhances the neural pathways in the brain for a particular thought. We must not forget that our thoughts are real – they produce electromagnetic and chemical signals across different networks of our brain cells. Also remember, it is only you who can talk to you inside your mind! We need these inner affirmations to help us through the many difficulties of today's world, with so much sadness, violence and ignorance – we need constant reminders of the positive, beautiful and true. They are the counterbalance. Just try this frequently for a few days and see how much better you feel – how released you feel.

You may like to repeat just one relevant word at regular moments throughout the day, such as peace, serenity, calm, tranquility, joy or love: or find your own special word. I often put two together; I quite frequently say to myself 'peace and love'. I know this sounds like a hippy greeting, but I find it very calming; it reminds me of what's really important, and it particularly helps me if I'm dealing with someone who is making me irritated or angry.

A helpful phrase I often use to myself is 'Rise above it!' My very wise father used to say that to me when I was young and would get into a state about someone, or something that upset me. It's a great statement and works on many levels. For me, it is like a comfort blanket; I surround myself with it, and mentally take off to the higher ground.

You might like to use my phrase, or you may find others that help you, such as:

- Do unto others as you would they do unto you.
- Silence is golden.
- To every thing there is a season, and a time to every purpose under heaven.
- Judge not, lest you yourself be judged.
- Life is meaningful when our hearts are full of love.
- or any of the ones in my list on pages 32–4.

I am reminded of the beautiful needlework samplers that used to hang in Victorian households with certain truths embroidered for inspiration or comfort. For example, 'Home is Where the Heart Is'. Use whatever feels appropriate for you. Use the ancient wisdoms as they were intended to be used – as a kind of life support system, or a blueprint from which everything ripples out. They change your inner state and as a result you have a different influence on those around you. This is how truth ripples out into the world, the planet and the universe.

You may not always be able to rise to the level of truth, but just knowing there is another way to see things, another way to behave, can release you from stress. In research studies a strong spiritual, religious or philosophical belief system has been discovered to be an important factor in maintaining good mental and physical health, and buffers one against stress – especially the stress of change or loss.

Writing things down makes them more real – whether words, sentences or paragraphs that contain a meaningful thought for you – it makes them physically manifest. Also, when you look at them you imprint them in your mind, as well as *reminding* yourself of their reality and truth. As I said above, they act as a counterbalance to the many dark and troubling images regularly presented to our minds through the media. I think we have to work at providing the *leitmotifs* for ourselves, to nourish and soothe our minds with good and uplifting thoughts and images. Carry them around with you in your pocket or bag and take them out to read from time to time, or simply touch the paper on which they are written and imagine the wise words being absorbed by your fingers, travelling up your arm and into your heart and mind – feel reassured just knowing what they tell you: let them strengthen you.

If you were not brought up in any belief system, or cannot connect with any customs or traditions, look at the positive aspect of this; it leaves you free to find your own belief structure, to mix and match different cultural thoughts or different spiritual beliefs in a way that makes sense to you. You are not constrained by just one belief system that dictates it is the 'right' one. I personally believe that all truth comes from the same source. I think all the religions in the world are talking about the same thing in different ways. There are many paths to the top of the mountain, but there is only one mountain top. So truth is truth in every language and in every different way it may be expressed. There are so many books around nowadays containing gems of wisdom and spiritual guidance from numerous sources. So, if you need inspiration visit your local bookstore and browse among the treasures and riches that have been put into print. Some are little pocket books, available at low cost, one or two of which you might find supportive to carry around with you. They will transport you to that other dimension we have been considering when you feel bogged down, overwhelmed, disillusioned, stressed. (See Further Reading.)

Your personal truth

Equally important, of course, are our own personal truths; whatever is valuable to you and sustains you in a personal way must not be neglected or lost along the way in the rush of daily living. It is important to honour consciously whatever you have recognised as a fundamental truth in your own experience of life, or simply whatever is significant in your own way of living your life. It could be the social customs or manners you were taught as a child, the 'rules' or guiding principles that were operating in your family, or possibly a particular member of your family or a teacher at school who inspired you with an inner desire to imitate their standards or achievements. As children we so often recognise the truths which transcend everyday concerns. As adults we must not lose the connection. We must remember what we have always known. I think our truths need to be polished up and put on display in our lives – like valuable possessions in a wealthy household. We must be proud of displaying our spiritual wealth. It is, after all, our valuable legacy from the past.

Alternatively, remember things which comforted or uplifted you when you were young, like special stories or poems, or particular toys that had a significant meaning for you – perhaps because they symbolised some positive quality like kindness, playfulness or joy and happiness; do not neglect them – hold on to whatever is of value to you. These are our personal comforters, which can encourage and reassure us when the going gets rough, and must be kept in place, in our inner world, alongside the innovative and new, in order that a right balance is maintained. It is important to keep the continuum, the connection to our personal and ancestral roots.

As I implied above, I believe that many of the answers to today's stress-inducing problems, and to questions about how to structure our lives, are to be found in the ancient wise teachings of all the different cultures: they can form a sort of bottom line, or the strong foundations upon which we can build and rebuild continuously. I feel they have even greater relevance for today than ever before, as they often restore a sense of calm and serenity that counterbalances the strain and rush.

It is important that we do not just race headlong into the future at great speed without a backward glance, throwing the baby out with the bath water and forgetting, neglecting or rejecting all that has been learnt by previous generations and other cultures – all the customs, traditions and beliefs that the wise elders recognised as essential to happiness. Many of today's problems exist because we are failing to include these fundamental cornerstones in much of modern life; we have destabilised ourselves. In the *Bhagavad-Gita* it is written:

> '*The wise say, My Lord! that they are forever lost, whose ancient traditions are lost.*'

We must find ways to apply wisdom teachings from the past in the modern context; this must form part of our strategy, otherwise we are left with insufficient familiar ground under our feet. It may be exciting to embrace and consume all that is new, but we are getting horribly out of balance.

Equally undesirable obviously, is that we over-react in the opposite direction by hanging on to the old ways no matter what, resisting and blocking everything which threatens to separate us from our comfortable preconceived ideas and habits. We should not feel threatened by the new, but equally we should not feel obliged to give up too readily all that has supported us previously. We need to give ourselves permission, and the confidence, to hold on to certain things and certain ways of doing things if they are right for us, in any of the areas of our lives, at the same time as opening ourselves to embrace the new age in which we live.

Recipes for life

It's a little like cooking a favourite recipe: usually if it is successful you have gradually learnt what extra ingredients to include, what ingredients to cut down on and what to leave out altogether because that's what suits your taste, and the taste of your family or friends. But if you leave out certain vital ingredients then the result will be disappointing. And if you handed on that incomplete recipe to future generations, they would never know the true taste of that particular dish unless someone remembered what had been forgotten and rewrote the recipe.

I do think we are currently in the process of creating a somewhat poisonous recipe for life; one that is definitely undernourishing, and which leaves out many essential ingredients. This must not be handed down to future generations: we must rethink what we are putting into the pot of daily life. What are we telling our children? Do we want to hand on recipes that are toxic? I am suggesting you rewrite the recipe for your life remembering not to leave out all that is true and valuable to you.

If this metaphor appeals to your imagination, you might like to sit down right now, take a piece of paper, and write out your recipe for living your life in the most fulfilled way possible. Then pin this recipe up in your kitchen, and every time you enter that room you will be reminded not to leave out the most important ingredients for a nourishing and sustaining lifestyle. If this feels too difficult then just list your own personal truths, as suggested above, to carry with you as a calming, de-stressing, inspirational checklist. Best of all, do both!

Below is a list of truths and wise teachings or sayings that I find inspiring, and which give me guiding principles for living my life. You may like to use this as a starting point for creating one of your own. Then add to it on an ongoing basis as you discover a truth which inspires, comforts or calms you, or when you remember some wise quotation from a book, a poem or a song, your Bible or any other spiritual teaching – or your mother.

My Personal List of Inspirational Wisdom and Eternal Truths

Always respond intelligently, even to unintelligent treatment – Chuang-Tzu

Do no harm – Buddhist teaching

He that findeth wisdom, findeth life – Proverbs

To love is to listen – American poet

To understand is to forgive – my own saying

All we have to do is become who we have always been – Carl Gustav Jung

This above all, to thine own self be true – William Shakespeare

Look after your body as if you will live for a thousand years, and your soul as if you will die tomorrow – Sufi teaching

---

Noblesse oblige – this means: with privilege comes responsibility

There's a lot of good in the worst of us
And a lot of bad in the best of us
So it ill behoves the most of us
To talk about the rest of us
– I love this little rhyme, quoted to me as a child

Live and let live – an important injunction for tolerance, for letting others be

In peace there is an end to all misery – Bhagavad-Gita

It is better to light one small candle than to bemoan the darkness – Carl Gustav Jung

If at first you don't succeed, try, try, try again – old wives' saying

Never let the sun go down upon your wrath – from the Bible: meaning we should try to resolve conflicts with others, or within ourselves, as soon as possible rather than carrying resentment and anger around with us for days, months or even years; very wise stress release

There is only one success: to be able to spend your life in your own way – Christopher Morley

As you sow, so shall you reap – Jesus of Nazareth

The fruit of love is service, which is compassion in action – Mother Teresa

All you need is love – The Beatles (one of the wisest sayings – ever!)

. . . and all the other quotes throughout this book

Returning to the recipe idea, below is an example of the sort of recipe you could create. Have fun with this, and with your list of truths. Enjoy connecting to your creativity. Especially, allow yourself to be still for a while, go quietly within and spend quality time reflecting on this important issue; connect to your own uniqueness and your own ideals. Even time spent thinking about what we have been discussing will separate you from the stresses of the world and give you a sense of serenity and peace.

A recipe for living

Mix 3 kilos of patience with 2 kilos of tolerance: leave to mature. Then add 3 large cups of loving kindness and 2 desertspoons of sweetness. Leave to stand for an hour or two. Blend in a large cupful of humour, a pinch of cynicism and 1 tablespoon of judgement. After 2 days taste for reality; then add 1 teaspoon of anger, 2 cups creativity, 3 cups flexibility and 1 tablespoon open-mindedness. Shake, don't stir.

You could get really creative and write out a recipe for each of the most important aspects of your life. For example: a recipe for raising children, a recipe for a wonderful holiday, a recipe for family life, a recipe for a productive work team, a recipe for a successful company, a recipe for a happy old age and so on. By working on this you cast a brighter light on what is important for you and you see yourself more clearly.

Do it your way

In more mundane terms this principle of not giving up everything from the past also applies. If some aspect of technology frustrates or confounds you, don't bother with it; use what you like and leave what you can't or don't want to handle. For example: if you prefer to continue to use the telephone rather than send e-mails, then assert your right, to yourself, to communicate in this way as much as you choose – in other words, in the way that suits you and your individual temperament. I read a lovely piece in a recent publication which was purported to have come originally from the actor and comedian Rowan Atkinson; he allegedly said that if e-mail had preceded the invention of the telephone, everyone would have hailed the arrival of said phone as the greatest technological breakthrough of recent times. He apparently added, 'Consider this: no longer do you have to type words into the ether hoping that someone will type back. You actually speak to someone on a gizmo that lets you and the recipient of your *bons mots* hear and talk to each other in real time!' This is exactly the kind of thinking that is needed to release our stresses – it is lateral thinking par excellence. In other words, thinking for oneself, rather than following the general consensus. Doing it your way!

To encourage you further, in the same publication Andrew Lloyd Webber revealed that he and Ben Elton always communicate with each other by fax as neither can do e-mails. Well, they are not greatly hampered in the success department by this inability, are they? What they are is confident enough to use what suits them and ignore what does not.

In another interview a well-known author revealed that she does not use a computer or word processor, as might be expected – or even a typewriter – but that she writes her books and film scripts in pencil, with a good old-fashioned rubber eraser near by. That's her way. We each have to find 'our own way': the way that is right for us. If the old ways work for you, think very carefully before abandoning them. Believe in yourself and in your own, unique, individual way.

Things do not necessarily have more value because they are new. Some of the old tools, or old attitudes, may be more useful or efficient, or life enhancing, than those that came after them. But make up your own mind. Don't allow yourself to be coerced into having to adopt every new gadget and technology that comes along just because it's there, hence loading yourself up with more to adjust to and learn, ever more stress and strain and ever less time. Also, don't allow technology to intimidate or overwhelm you. Keep reminding yourself that it is all there to act as your slave, not the other way round! And when your machines – like printers, photocopiers, computers – break down, don't automatically assume that it is somehow you who are inadequate. Machines do break down, it is all part of the stress of life, and the only thing you can do is not overload yourself with guilt about it; accept it and be patient, especially with yourself.

Today's world requires constant discrimination, and we are going to have to exercise it very powerfully in order not to lose control of our lives, our joy, and our dreaming/creative time. We have to find a stance that is open to the new, but not destabilised by being empty because we have thrown out all the old valuables.

'And/and' not 'either/or'

In psychology there is an idea that could be applied usefully here: it is the notion of 'and/and' rather than 'either/or'. What this means is that instead of putting things in opposition to each other, and then having to decide which is better, or more desirable than the other – possibly causing yourself much inner turmoil and conflict – you adopt an inclusive stance of embracing them both at the same time. In other words, of seeing that the merits of one do not negate the merits of the other; that each has a place. One may be right at one time, or in a certain situation, and the other at another time or in other circumstances. Or both may be 'best' in different ways. This really is very freeing.

Whenever you find yourself in a dilemma of duality, with the question, 'Is it this, or is it that?' try answering yourself with, 'It's both,' and see if this makes the situation both easier and clearer. Or if you are asking yourself, 'Should I do this or that?' answer, 'Both,' and see what a difference it makes to the tension and stress. I don't mean that you should load yourself up with more and more things to do, but that you ease the inner stress by seeing how two seemingly opposing things can both be the right way to proceed; maybe you can even mix them together, with a little from one and something from the other to arrive at a more creative outcome. The more you are able to grasp and adopt this 'and/and' principle in your life, the more you will find a way through potential conflicts. So often we get caught up in the ping-pong thrust of 'no, it isn't' – 'yes, it is': or 'I'm right!' – 'No you're not, I am!', which gets us nowhere.

There is no *one* right way of doing things, but many right ways. We need a variety of ideas and insights and we need the flexibility to embrace many possibilities. Flexibility is going to be one of the most important attributes to foster in the coming years.

Find the 'Third Point'

Much has been heard lately of the notion of the 'third way', and much scorn has also been heaped upon it. Nevertheless, I think there is such a thing as the 'third way'; that it is actually a third point that stands between, and a little apart from, the old and the new (or any extremes), and assesses dispassionately what is valuable about both. The way to approach this concept is to find a third point that stands above the conflicting duality of either/or, and from here you will be able to lift yourself out of the tension in a situation and to look at it more objectively from above. Think of yourself standing at the apex of a triangle, above the duality, and from here you are able to see that everything is part of the whole. In other words, that everything has a place. This is enormously releasing.

We need to find a balanced path between the old ideas and practices and the new innovations, valuing what is good in each. I think this is our challenge at this moment in history – to get the mix right between the past that is worth retaining – the wisdom of past generations – and the new ideas that are born from a future vision. It is important in any situation that you attempt to hold this balance, retaining what is good while welcoming what is new, rather than allowing one automatically to negate the other.

An exercise for maintaining equilibrium

Whenever you are in crisis, stress or confusion imagine yourself standing upright, well balanced, with your arms held out at either side of your body. Picture one side of you as holding the present and the other side as holding the past. Picture your legs and feet firmly placed on the ground and your body perfectly balanced between the two extremes; especially feel yourself anchored securely in all that you know to be true and right from past experience, then open yourself up to the new situation, or new information, or whatever is confronting you at that moment. Don't be destabilised by forgetting to hold on to what you already know. We are often thrown into the panic of feeling ourselves in a vacuum of nothingness when we feel stressed or anxious. So support yourself by affirming all that you know to be true. Then be receptive to whatever else is demanding your attention.

You can strengthen the inner balance that results from this exercise by actually, physically standing in the position you have just imagined, and then go through the visualisation again. Put your physical body into an upright posture: stand with your feet slightly apart, firmly planted on the ground and your arms outstretched at either side, away from your body. Feel yourself perfectly balanced. Now feel the certainty of all you know moving in a vertical line through your body, from your head to your heart, and then all through your body down to your feet; now up through your heart to your head again. This is a centring experience. The experience goes all through you and is not just in your head. So whatever is pulling at you on either side – whether from the past, present or future – it does not have the power to destabilise you.

All of this chapter is aimed at helping you to a state of greater equilibrium within yourself. Use these suggestions in your own way, but heed the message: do not throw the baby out with the bath water!

3

Who is in control?

One of the truths that does not change however much the external circumstances change, is that as members of the species *homo sapiens* we have very distinct and fundamental needs which have to be met if we are to feel relatively happy or contented, anxiety free, comfortable and well. Not paying sufficient attention to any of these needs will make us more susceptible to stress.

We have already identified our need for some things to remain the same as a stabilising bedrock in a climate of change, also the need to retain the wisdom of the past and our connection to truth, as well as the need to stay within the limit of our adaptation energy. Another of our most important basic needs is to feel in control of our lives and ourselves. Feeling out of control, or without sufficient control, is one of the major triggers to feeling stressed, and has been found to have negative implications for health.

Knowing that you have a satisfactory level of control over the world around you is good for your immune system and your heart. It has been demonstrated in experiments with animals that having no control over various stress factors suppressed immune function to a significant degree, while animals subjected to the same stresses, but given some control over them, did not suffer the same internal damage. Also in one long-term study of a colony of monkeys those creatures who had little or no control over the ordering of the hierarchy, and who were continually dominated by larger, more powerful monkeys, eventually developed high blood pressure, followed by heart disease, due to the clogging up of their coronary arteries. This was despite eating the same diet, living in the same habitat and having the same degree of physical freedom as the higher status animals. In other words, the only difference was in their total lack of control over their environment and the behaviour towards them by others in the society. The high-status monkeys had unclogged arteries. There was an unexpected discovery, however. Some of the low-status monkeys managed to find a role for themselves by grooming their superiors and acting as helpers, with some of the low-status males playing with the young, baby monkeys (it is normally unheard of for young males to take any interest in babies). However, by doing this, they developed less severe atherosclerosis than those monkeys who were cowed by, and acquiesced to, their powerlessness. This seemed to point to the fact that if you can exercise a degree of autonomy, even in oppressive conditions, there will be less damage to your health.

A similar study, on civil servants, called the Whitehall Study, was carried out by London University, over a period of 30 years. To their surprise, the lowest occurence of heart disease was found among the highest level employees, who they had thought would be suffering from so-called 'executive stress'. However, those people at the 'top' had a high degree of control, which seemed to induce good health. Heart disease rates got worse as you went down the grades. It was discovered that death rates were three times higher among junior office workers than among the senior civil servants. Only 40 per cent of this difference could be explained by lifestyle factors, that is diet, exercise and smoking. It was concluded that the longer life expectancy in the more senior ranks was 60 per cent due to having a high level of control and high status in the hierarchy. Similar conclusions have been drawn from other studies. High status, of course, implies control and autonomy: the freedom to make your own decisions and not feel oppressed, controlled or blocked by others.

A disturbing paradox of modern life, however, is that while we have increasing numbers of gadgets and technologies supposedly designed to give us freedom and independence, at the same time we are discovering that we actually have less and less control over numerous aspects of our lives. I believe we need to address this very consciously. The more aware we make ourselves of our stress factors, the more we can alter our behaviours and internal responses, both physiologically and attitudinally, so that they do not damage our health.

A great deal of the stress experienced today, and its outward expression of anger, is connected with the expectation that we should be able to control things, but in fact we can't! We own motor cars – once seen as ultimate symbols of independence and freedom – but we cannot drive them comfortably because too many other people also own cars and slow us down to a snail's pace or get in our way! We have developed wondrous modes of communication, but it is increasingly frustrating trying to get hold of a human being at the end of a telephone line, without having to listen to endless recorded instructions about pressing buttons while wasting huge amounts of time. Not to mention e-mails that are not answered and faxes that are not received!

In a sense we have set ourselves up. We have come to rely more and more on machines, gadgets and gizmos, which, when they don't work as they are supposed to, put us into a state of impotence. In addition, many of the structures and organisations that direct and control the various facets of modern living, or which are supposed to serve us, have become so huge and centralised, bogged down in bureaucracy and procedures, that they can make us feel threatened, or powerless and overwhelmed by the difficulty of trying to interact with them. We certainly do not often feel that we can control them, or even the way they treat us.

We are confronted daily by frustration due to this increasing lack of control which, if it has no outlet or is not handled in the right way, can lead to a range of health problems including digestive disorders, irritable bowel syndrome, duodenal ulcers, disordered breathing patterns, panic attacks: all manifestations of inner tensions. It is extremely important that we learn some strategies for handling the internal anger that is, quite understandably, triggered by the stress of not being able to have the level of control we would like. Internal anger as a result of feeling disempowered often leads to depression; our energy and enthusiasm are suppressed.

In this chapter we are going to look at ways of altering our attitudinal approach, so as not to damage our health, and in Chapters 6 and 7 you will find the physical side addressed. You will find relaxation techniques and suggestions for releasing tension, as well as a detailed explanation of why getting wound up creates problems for the heart. Potentially damaging physiological changes take place within our bodies when we become stressed and frustrated, or feel threatened in some way, and I shall suggest ways in which you can take more control of these responses, so that you can choose to react in the way that is best for your health and wellbeing.

Strategy No. 1

When you absolutely cannot control a situation, the best and healthiest way of coping is to practice **acceptance**. If there is nothing you can do about it, let it go. Don't get wound up and angry, because you will jeopardise your health and not solve the problem.

Recognising when there is nothing you can do is wisdom. There is no point resisting something that you cannot change, like a traffic jam, a delayed plane or train or a machine that refuses to respond: it just winds you up and wastes your energy. Acceptance is not resignation, it is the recognition of reality, not denying that something is as it is. And in fact, once you practice acceptance you often begin to find ways around the situation, or whatever is facing you, because you are no longer putting all your energy and focus into the resistance and denial. Acceptance relaxes you. When you are relaxed you are more in harmony with yourself, and can connect more freely with your creativity and innovation.

I am reminded of the serenity prayer which was so popular a few years ago. It may seem a little clichéd now, but the message is sound. Let me remind you:

> *'Lord, grant me the **Serenity** to accept those things that I cannot change;*
> *The **Courage** to change the things I can;*
> *And the **Wisdom** to know the difference.'*

It might strike a chord with some of you, and the thoughts are sensible stress release. You might like to write it down and carry it around with you or pin it up in your home or work space, or wherever you feel the most frustration in your life – perhaps your car! Or keep it in your pocket to read when faced with yet another delayed train.

John Betjeman, our late Poet Laureate, who was also a knowledgeable commentator on architecture, once said to me, 'The trouble with skyscrapers is that they bear no relationship whatsoever to the proportions of the human body, and therefore we cannot relate to them with any sense of comfort.' Isn't this true of so much of today's world? It is out of proportion in relation to individual human beings, and many people when faced with these giant corporations and huge impersonal civic structures feel alienated, confused or uninvolved. This phenomenon can be seen in the diminishing numbers of the electorate who turn out to vote, for example. Or in the way we 'blank' each other in much of our daily activity – walking down busy streets, standing in supermarket queues, or on a crowded train or bus when thrust into close encounters of the embarrassing kind with total strangers!

I think it is a terrible shame that we treat other people as if they don't exist, but this seems to be the only way we can cope with much of today's world. It is all so big that it is difficult to relate to, and we can't control it! We feel disempowered and therefore we opt out; it is often easier to say to ourselves that we just don't care, rather than to struggle with the feeling of being ineffectual.

Strategy No. 2

If you feel unable to control a situation sufficiently, and you cannot accept it or find a way round it, another healthy reaction may be to decide to turn your back on it. That way you have taken back the control and decided on the action you will take. This is empowering. Walking away, or cutting off from something, may be the wisest choice you can make at that time.

There certainly seems to be an increasing tendency to withdraw more and more into our own personal, smaller worlds and this is very sensible practice in certain circumstances. I would always advise that you withdraw for a while when you feel overwhelmed, because we cannot take on the whole world, the whole time. However, when carried to extremes, enclosing ourselves too exclusively in our own worlds can – and does – have negative consequences for local communities, as well as for us individually. The more we cut ourselves off from each other, the more we encourage misunderstanding. The answer is to take control in the right ways and not be pushed into reactionary measures or extreme positions.

Strategy No. 3

Another way to feel more in control generally is in taking decisions: when we make the right decisions we feel in control. Not perhaps of the situation or circumstances, but of ourselves and our actions, and sometimes that is the only control we can have. Or, if it is appropriate, deciding on a plan of action for making some changes that will give us more control, and beginning to implement the action, is always empowering.

We can also make a decision to put ourselves into more situations where we *can* exercise control, to balance out the areas where we have little or no power. This could be in leisure-time activities like sport, where we can control our own performance, or in creative activities and hobbies, which give greater scope for controlling our timetables and the way we set about tasks. Another important decision would be to make sure we spend more time with people with whom we feel equal, and with the people who listen to us and respect our right to have a say about a situation or an outcome. This allows us to be more fully our true self, which is always empowering.

It is extremely important to remember that we always have the option of taking control of ourselves: of our actions and reactions, as well as our inner attitudes.

One important attitude may be to bring humour into the situation to defuse it.

The stress of capitalism and the consumer society

Of course, we can't opt out forever, or continually walk away, these are strategies to release stress in the moment. Sooner or later we have to opt back in again. We have to go back out there and resume the struggle with all of the above. In the long term, we may have to adjust our thinking in order to cope with the environment in which we now find ourselves. Because we live in the middle of it, it is difficult to stand back and analyse it very clearly. But I think the more we can become aware of how we are 'set up' the more we can do to change the way we relate to it. For, even if you can't change the outside world, you can change the way you interact with it, and this is the next strategy I want to put before you.

Most of us live in the capitalist or 'consumer' society, and the very nature of this society puts great pressure on all of us. The important point about the capitalist system is that it *needs* to control us if it is to function successfully; it must seduce us, or manipulate us, into maximum consumption. This is another aspect of the stress of today's world that I believe we need to address consciously. We are under incessant commercial pressure, which causes subliminal stresses and anxieties, due to the subtle coercion on our conscious control and the activating of our insecurities.

The consumer myth

To keep us engaged or to entice us back into the relationship, large, impersonal organisations and civic authorities put out cosy, intimate advertisements to lull us into believing that they relate to us as individuals; we are cosseted and wooed as if we mattered when, in truth, we are only related to as figures on a balance sheet. This explains the bad service, and extra frustration, you receive from those 'lovely people' in that television ad. The company and the advertisement are unconnected; it is all part of the manipulation, the mirage that is created to part you from your money – it is the consumer myth – and, again, you have no control over it. But worse, it is having a stressful influence on you. It undermines your self-esteem. For, no matter how much we all realise that the unrealistic promises implied in many ads are pure fantasy creations, if you absorb an image on a regular basis it will eventually make a lasting impression.

When we continually see perfect-looking people with enviable lifestyles, it is bound to make us feel anxious about how well we are doing in our own lives, and unhappy with ourselves when we know how far away we are from those beautiful people with perfect hair, perfect teeth, perfect bodies, living in gleamingly clean luxurious homes, with that expensive car in the driveway! It takes a strong person to stand apart from it all, someone with a very powerful sense of self. The pressure to be more physically perfect and have more things creates discontentment and erodes inner peace, causing much unconscious stress, as well as tempting people to spend more than they can afford, leading on to loss of financial control.

This may all seem obvious, but the important point is that we acknowledge consciously to ourselves just what is happening, why we feel these frustrations or impotency and where we feel them most – in which parts of our daily lives. If we can identify the sources of our stress triggers we can diminish their impact. When something is having an unconscious influence on us it is at its most powerful – you cannot deal with an unseen adversary or an unacknowledged one. It is a little like a food allergy: if you can identify which food is causing the undesirable symptoms you can eliminate it from your diet. If, however, you do not know what is causing your symptoms then you are a victim of them.

We are in a conundrum of conflict in today's world – empowered and disempowered at the same time. This lies at the heart of much of the stress we experience. And it applies to all of us, both in the developed and developing countries, for we have been given to expect much – at all levels of society – and yet delivery is somehow always happening tomorrow. Contentment eludes us. But, of course, we are looking for contentment in the wrong place, and I shall expand on this later.

It is important to realise that our materialist society is not interested in fulfilling us, it is merely interested in fulfilling its own objectives: profits! Each individual is only seen as a unit of ingestion, as a consumer of as much as possible, in order to maximise those profits. The way this is achieved, of course, is to seduce us with the illusion that we will find fulfilment and contentment in acquiring more and more things. This is fine if we understand the game that is being played. If not, we could increasingly feel like victims in the face of these trends. This is why it is so important to take up this issue consciously.

When we see things for what they are, then we can deal with them more effectively and have the possibility of taking control. If we are in control, we will understand the consumer trick; we will of course purchase the things we need but we will not get hung up on consuming for any other reason than our genuine need. How much of what we buy is a genuine need? An opinion survey by the Harwood Group in the USA for the Merck Family Fund, entitled 'Yearning for Balance', found 82 per cent of Americans agreeing that 'most of us buy and consume far more than we need; it's wasteful'. Another recent research study among 1,400 people, led by Dr Shaun Saunders of the University of Newcastle, New South Wales, found that the more materialistic an individual is, the more likely he or she is to be depressed, angry and dissatisfied with life. Dr Saunders said, 'Retail therapy provides a hollow form of fulfilment, something transient which is not compatible with a lifetime of happiness . . . someone else will always have more possessions, and this can lead to frustration and feelings of helplessness.'

What do you need?

Each time you buy anything, ask yourself which need this fulfils. It may be, for example, that your answer is that you are fulfilling a need of vanity. Well then, ask yourself, do you need this need! If the answer is 'yes', then go ahead and feed the need. But at least know why you are consuming. Then you are in control. But it may also be that you recognise that you do not genuinely need this item, and so you can free yourself up from the tyranny of the consumer myth. The more you are able to free yourself from colluding with consumerism the lighter you will feel, and the less stressed you will be.

It is time to take back the control. We have to stop being led like sheep into believing that we must accommodate every invention simply because it has been invented, or that we must obey every fashion and whim thought up by commercial interests to take our money from us. All endorsed by the media, of course, with the same intention of parting us from our dosh! In order that we are not reduced to robots or puppets controlled by state and commerce we have to begin to choose to opt out a little more.

We live in a situation like 'The Emperor's New Clothes'. We are all buying into something (in more ways than one!) that many of us suspect is deeply questionable, if not an outright deception, but somehow we fail to voice our misgivings lest we seem out of step, foolish or naïve. We have to find the courage of the small child to see the situation for what it is.

Who controls your mind?

I do not think we pay enough attention to the daily attempt to control our minds by the media, the advertising industry and the opinion makers in various walks of life. We take it all for granted, but if we were to visit another planet for a few months and then return to Earth, I think we would be amazed at the level of bombardment our minds receive from the various media – television, radio, newspapers, magazines, advertising posters, unsolicited mail, the Internet and so on. I remember returning to London a few years ago, after a month's holiday staying in the very peaceful and slow-paced countryside of Gran Canaria, and feeling almost blown away by the billboards, posters and neon-lit words all screaming some sort of promotion at me as I journeyed through the streets towards home.

I think we should be more alarmed about this – if not outraged. We are subjected to subliminal messages all through our waking hours; they are received by our unconscious minds and cause a lot of conflict and confusion below the surface of consciousness. In a recent television documentary about the advertising industry it was stated that we are exposed to 1,200 advertising messages per day. This creates anxiety, nervousness, jitteriness and fidgetiness. Any sensory input that we do not receive consciously and assimilate with interest makes us nervous, and has a destructive effect on our nervous systems, often leading to insomnia – a condition that is spreading like an epidemic in our civilisation.

Of course, I know that subliminal advertising is prohibited by law, but the overt messages all carry many subtle levels of meaning within them, which we all recognise but somehow collude with. When told, 'You must have this fantastic car, this amazing shampoo & conditioner, this soft, long toilet paper, this face cream, this particular soft drink, that particular make of jeans, this exotic holiday' . . . and so on, the subtext is, 'It will make you feel successful, superior, valuable, acceptable – a member of the "In Group"; and if you cannot afford these things, or fail to acquire them for whatever reason, you are a failure, a nobody, a non-member of society, definitely not a member of any acceptable group.' Who says? Who exactly are the people telling you what to buy, wear and eat, and where to take your holidays? Are they people of superior judgement, exquisite taste and higher knowledge? Of course not!

We are being dumped on

The point is that we are allowing ourselves to be dumped on continuously. And this is the really important point. So much of our current culture is just a great big dump! No wonder we are stressed; no wonder we are depressed; no wonder we are unfulfilled! We are dumped on continuously with other people's agendas – and they are not friendly agendas, they are manipulative, self-interested agendas. Not in the least bit concerned with our best interests. We are so used to it that we have become somewhat anaesthetised and desensitised to what is actually happening. We take it all in, pretty well uncensored, and obey. The way we are being controlled and manipulated is insidious and subtle, but those forces create a great deal of pressure on our minds and emotions. Those subliminal messages play on us, creating doubts and undermining our confidence, as well as promising counterfeit happiness.

We cannot eliminate these elements of our culture, but we can alter our reaction to them; we can be more aware of how much we allow them to influence us.

Counter measures

One of the ways to counteract this insidious influence is to cut down your consumption of media. Do not buy a newspaper every day – give your mind a break! Do you really need to know all that depressing news and gossip churned out daily to boost sales? A major part of the stress and tension we all feel is due to not spending enough time on inner reflection; our attention is focused too much on the outer world and not enough on the inner world of thoughts, feelings and imagination. This creates unbalance and much mental tiredness. So another part of our strategy has to be in rethinking our habits.

Instead of reading the newspaper or a magazine while commuting, for example, close your eyes and imagine beautiful pictures: beautiful places that you know and love, or somewhere you create in your imagination. It can be somewhere in nature: a park, a garden or a beach, or it could be a perfect room, filled with the objects and furniture you would love to have around you. Or just picture one beautiful and uplifting object like a waterfall, a tree, a flower, a crystal, a cross, a sunset, the sea, a rainbow – anything that brings you joy. You will be amazed how much less tired you will feel. Just try it for a few days and start yourself on a new habit. This is the way to begin the practice of meditation. For meditation is really just an inner concentration of the mind; it alters the speed of your brain waves and is stabilising and refreshing for the mind.

Don't worry if your mind will not stay on the inner image for long, but keeps wandering off to thinking about the more mundane concerns of your life; just gently bring it back to your chosen visualisation each time you realise it has strayed. Do not become angry with yourself, or with your mind, or despairing of your ability to concentrate. You have to train the mind in the same way as you would train a young animal; you must be very patient and gentle, and just keep on persevering. The more you practice this exercise, the more power you will gain over your mind. The benefits of this greater control will ripple out into the rest of your life, as you will find your powers of concentration improving and you will be able to focus on what *you* decide, not on what your mind decides to present to you. You become increasingly the master of your mind, and this means you will also have more control over negative or fearful thoughts: you will simply be able to say, 'No, thank you! I don't want to think that right now.' So get into the habit of practicing these visualisations whenever you have a little space, or when you are feeling particularly stressed and strained; it is a wonderful way to bring in more calm and to bring about a disengagement with the outer world. This allows you to realign yourself, and gain a fresh perspective.

Do not turn on the TV every day or every evening as an automatic reaction when you get home. Would that be so hard? If so, maybe you should question what this addiction really means. Personally, I find that having some days in the week when I do not tune in to television is a great help in maintaining inner equilibrium and peace of mind and spirit. It gives you the chance to create your own world, your own atmosphere, rather than endlessly partaking of other people's ideas, conflicts or problems. There are so many alternatives to watching passively while other people perform and I really believe everyone would feel much better if they reduced their television consumption. Apart from resting your senses from bombardment, think of the time it would free up. You would have more time for many other pursuits that perhaps you wish you could enjoy. Like listening to your favourite music; reading all those novels, history books, autobiographies or self-development books you keep saying you want to; creating a beautiful garden, or reorganising your home environment; learning another language; talking to your partner; listening to your children! Or just having time to drift and dream. It would give you back a sense of being more in control of you, because you would not be consuming such a large portion of other people's agendas. My suggestion is that you start by trying to have one day a week when you do not turn on your TV. Be firm with yourself and stick with it until you have broken the automatic habit of turning to your television to entertain you. It could be a different day each week but just stick with the principle that at least one day in the week the box does not go on! That probably sounds unthinkable, but give it a try and see if you feel that you have somehow reclaimed your life a little.

The same applies to the radio, although I don't consider it such a negative influence because we have to exercise our imagination in the absence of visual images, which is important because it brings something from ourselves – from our creative mind – into the moment. But having the radio on in the background, and not really listening to it, is very tiring for your mind. Just giving half-attention to anything is more fatiguing than giving your full attention and it is also disturbing for the nervous system as it cannot make full sense of what it is receiving.

Try to feel comfortable with silence. It is wonderfully restful for the mind. It is also amazing how many creative and imaginative thoughts arise in the absence of someone else's agenda. This is why so many people have their best ideas in the bath or shower – it is often the only time in their day when they are removed from media and other people's input. Trust yourself to feel OK without constant outside help.

Of course, it takes a strong person to buck a trend, but that is how we release ourselves from stress. By becoming stronger in our own convictions. As a result we are less likely to be coerced by somebody else's. We have to set our own agenda.

We imagine that we are not really affected by these influences, we are too sensible, too individual, too in control! Well, maybe. But just consider how much you are influenced by fashion. Be honest with yourself! How much do you worry that you have not seen the latest play, or film, not dined in one of the latest trendy restaurants, not been to the new hip bar, not bought one of the latest fashion accessories or gadgets for your home, not seen that popular TV programme or read that acclaimed new novel or clever self-help book? Or that you have not stuck to the latest fashionable diet, or started the exercise programme you know you 'should' do, or joined that Yoga class that is so popular with the film stars and other famous personalities? What a lot of baggage we carry around!

Do you see how we overload ourselves by being slaves to other people's control? I am not saying don't allow yourself to want things; just be sure that it is for the right reasons – your own individual, personal reasons, and not that you are keeping up with someone else's idea of what you should be 'consuming'.

All of this commercial pressure to have more, achieve more, keep up with the 'in crowd', and so on, just adds to the feelings of stress that we already have to contend with in our personal lives. It's like this: how much control do you have over your children's sleeping patterns, their eating likes and dislikes, your partner's requirements, your boss's demands, your mother's neuroses, your father's moods, or your dog's incontinence? Do you see what I am getting at? There is so much of it all! We just have to draw the line. We need to start taking more control and deciding for ourselves how much we really want to go along with, collude with, or acquiesce to. We need to decide a little more consciously how much we wish to play the game. Indeed, how much of the game we are entering willingly – and to what extent we are there against our better judgement, because we think we 'should' be.

I see so many people – young and not so young, married and single, female and male – who are not happy because they are buying into someone else's idea of what they 'should' look like or what they 'should' be achieving or what kind of lover they 'should' have or what kind of person they 'ought' to be. Much of this pressure to do and be what is not really right for them as individuals is coming from society's messages via the media, advertising and so on. But those sources are not the slightest bit interested in your wellbeing – they are interested in the health of their balance sheets, their profits. Remember that. Realise also that the level of consumption that is encouraged by commercial advertising is actually unsustainable, and so contributes not only to personal stress but to global problems as well.

Kevin Costner said in a recent TV interview: 'It seems as if the world is asleep at the wheel!' I absolutely agree with him. We really must wake up. We have to develop more confidence in ourselves, and set our own agendas. Do not allow a particular brand to tell you that you must possess it. What madness is this?

The market place exploits your insecurities and fears by making you feel inadequate, that you are not good enough, so that you have to buy more and more to feel OK. When our insecurities are triggered, they are in control. Therefore we need to check out frequently which part of ourselves is really in control. Is it the child within that feels little and powerless, and who needs an outside authority to set the agenda, or the part that feels unattractive and the wrong shape, or is it the internal parent voice telling you that you are worthless, stupid, no good? We all have many sub-personalities that vie for control within us. When one of these has been triggered, and you're feeling insecure, call up in your mind's eye a picture of yourself at some time when you felt really good about yourself, when you felt truly your 'best self'. Then affirm to yourself that this is who you are – this is your true potential, waiting to be realised at any moment you choose. If you've been there once there's no reason why you can't be there again, right now – or any time you choose. We so often put blocks in our own way and trip ourselves up, or undermine ourselves with our negative self-talk. So keep affirming inwardly that picture of you as your most sublime and powerful self.

Live lightly in the world

Another approach to the consumer society is to take the attitude promoted by many Eastern philosophies:

> 'Be in the world but not of the world.'

The way I see this being put into practice is to live alongside the world of stress, demand and commercial seduction, not right in the middle of it. That doesn't mean you have to live way out of the city, in the middle of nowhere; it means changing the focus of your attention. It means concentrating your energy, enthusiasm, imagination and interest on all that is not part of the materialistic, corporate world, more often than perhaps you do at present. As I have already said, try to limit how much commercialism you take into your brain, and how much space it occupies on your agenda, and include more that is artistic, imaginative, spiritual, soulful, natural and free. Give equal weight and value to these other aspects of life. Practice dis-identifying with the commercial world, and the dictates of that world; release your attachment to the things that can cause you stress. By this, I do not mean you have to stop doing anything you were doing before – just release your attachment to it, dependence on it and identification with it. Greater serenity and 'centredness' is achieved by beginning to identify with something more eternal, substantial and less transitory, and to spend more time thinking about it, learning about it, reading about it, practicing it. This links back into what I said in Chapter 2 about your own truths and values. It is on that level that you find peace and happiness of a more sustaining kind, and it creates a counterbalance that will give you more resources with which to tackle everyday life. If you can slowly develop a greater degree of non-attachment to the material world, you will feel an increased calm in the face of problems.

This is not a rejection of anything, it is simply a shift of position, so that your relationship with the transient becomes more distant, more disengaged, more detached – more free. It is in letting go that we can find our own release. (There is more on how to do this in the next chapter.)

One of my personal philosophies is not to become too attached to, or depend too much on, anything that can be taken away from me; not to rely too much on something that someone else, or circumstances, can suddenly remove. I gain my support from, among other things, my inner life of meditation and thinking, my enjoyment of music, poetry, literature and particularly the joy I derive from experiencing nature in all its myriad forms.

I do believe there is much truth in the adage that the best things in life are free. And this is especially true with regard to all the natural wonders of the world. Take some time to contemplate the natural beauty around you. Recognise that we are always in nature, we don't necessarily have to make special trips out into the countryside. Just look up at the sky more often, its changing shapes and colours are a wonderful sight for sore eyes! Let the vastness of it transport you for a moment or two, and enlarge your perspective on your world. It's important to take the time to stand back and stare – in awe and wonder at the magnificence, complexity and beauty of it all, and in gratitude at what we have been given. Remember the words of the famous poem by W. H. Davies:

> 'What is this life if, full of care, we have no time to stand and stare?'

So, nourish and uplift yourself by standing and staring as often as you can! Walk in parks and admire and appreciate the creative work that goes into making them beautiful for you to enjoy; walk along the riverbank, or beside a canal, and discover a new and amazing world of 'water people' and water wildlife. Also, of course, try to get away from the concrete city and immerse yourself in the deep countryside as much as possible, or at the beach and the sea – to feast your senses and to reconnect with the bigger picture.

Pioneer researcher Dr Hans Selye, who I mentioned in Chapter 1, wrote in his book, *The Stress Of Life*, 'The most harmonious and mysterious creations are those of Nature; and to my mind, it is the highest cultural aim of the professional scientist to interpret that so that others may share in their enjoyment . . . there is an equanimity and a peace of mind which can be achieved only through contact with the sublime.'

Instead of seeing yourself as a citizen of the materialist society, try thinking of yourself as a citizen of the natural world. That is, everything in the planet that is natural and beautiful, and not man-made. Claim your place within all that miraculous beauty. Because truly we are creatures of nature, of the natural world. Many of our current problems arise from the fact that we have forgotten this. When we put ourselves outside nature, then we can exploit and destroy it. In my opinion we are identifying with the wrong side! Yes, we are all responsible to a greater or lesser degree for our current world, but if we could step back and observe it all a little more objectively we might live more lightly in it.

Treat it all as a joke, or a game not to be taken too seriously, that you pack up at the end of the day, and can begin again in the morning if you choose. Learn to laugh at it. Consume it lightly, but don't let it consume you. Don't be controlled by the market place. The market place doesn't care about you – it is out to exploit you. Of course we need the market place for transactions to take place, but that's all – that's all! American university professor of business administration, Ralph Estes, says in his book, *Tyranny of the Bottom Line: Why corporations make people do bad things* (Berrett-Koehler), that business is a system originally created to serve the public interest, but it has gone astray through an unbalanced focus on profit, a 'perverse score-keeping system' that measures a company's effects on stockholders but not on employees, customers or the larger community. Commerce has forgotten its original intentions and *raison d'etre*. So do not identify with it too completely. See it merely as a convenience, not the last resort. Keep your distance. We take it too seriously. The market place is not the final destination. Remember the words of the poet Wordsworth:

> *'The world is too much with us; late and soon,*
> *Getting and spending, we lay waste our powers.'*

Can you imagine how differently the world stage would look if we prioritised inner development above outer, material growth? If we valued wisdom more than wealth? We could do it. Humankind could decide to change the focus. Who says we must worship material wealth? Why not worship natural resources? Or beauty? Why not say that the winners in life are the ones with the most beautiful countries and the least damaged natural habitats? Does it sound so crazy? We could certainly do with a shift in balance towards that other side.

Visualising a different world

Picture two roads: one that is full of the activity of the market place, the average High Street; and the other a country road typical of those in France, bordered by trees with fields stretching away into the distance. See yourself walking down the country road; that is the true path of your life because you are a part of the natural world. Think of the other one as a place you visit from time to time, as you choose. But always you return at the close of day to the place of tranquility, in nature and peace. Hold those two roads in your imagination and get used to seeing them as the two possibilities of your life. You can travel down one or the other, as you choose, but you must always come home to the tranquil road. Now create in your imagination a picture of a beautiful sanctuary – somewhere you would like to be, that would soothe and refresh you. Then place your sanctuary somewhere along the country road – and know that this is a place into which you can withdraw whenever you feel in need of peace and solace; it is your natural home – the special place within yourself to which you can return regularly. This will provide the balance to the market place.

In *Siddhartha*, Hermann Hesse writes, 'Within you there is a stillness and sanctuary to which you can retreat at any time and be yourself.' This sanctuary is an inner awareness of comfort. An inner feeling of ease that cannot be disturbed by turmoil or distress. With practice of visualisation and relaxation it is possible for everyone to experience this state within. It is also the state one experiences in meditation.

'*Manifest plainness,*
Embrace simplicity,
Reduce selfishness,
Have few desires.' Lao-Tzu

4

Take control of
your agenda

'Stress as overload' is a definition I find most people relate to and grasp immediately. I usually give the example of imagining yourself carrying a number of items, say on a tray, which you can manage perfectly well until someone comes along and loads a few more, rather large items on top of what is already there. The tray now becomes quite heavy but you can still cope by tightening your muscles and bracing yourself. However, two more people appear and each place an extra, extremely heavy item on top of everything else and suddenly you are beyond the limit of your strength and you drop the lot! The relevant point is that you were carrying most of the things quite easily; it was only when the last one or two were added that you dropped everything. And this is what happens in our lives – we can cope happily up to a certain point, with a certain amount; but if pushed beyond the limit of our resources too frequently, or for too long, we can suddenly become incapable of coping with anything at all. We drop the lot!

This image of overload cannot easily be rejected, or denied. Too much overloading – whether physical or mental – and something has to give. This is a very good description of what is happening to many when they say they feel stressed. They are being pushed beyond their limit – that is, overloaded beyond the limit of the resources they have available to respond and deal comfortably with whatever life throws up.

Too much on your agenda?

This is where we start to talk about your agenda. So many people feel their agendas are overloaded: this is something I hear all the time. Why? And who is loading them up? Why are we piling more and more onto ourselves? We need to ask this question; but we also need to be helped to offload. This is an essential key to our greater wellbeing. If you put too much onto your agenda, you may find that even the easy things feel difficult, because you are overloaded. Too much is too much, whatever its nature!

People often say to me, 'What I am doing is not very difficult, so I shouldn't make a fuss about feeling stressed.' Well no, it may not be difficult but it can still be too much! You only have so many hours in a day, and it is important to become clear about how you want to spend those hours. A lot of what we do, and think, can be classed as clutter, trivia or unnecessary. When I say unnecessary, I mean this in terms of your true goals and aims; the same applies to the other two words – clutter and trivia. If we spend time on things which will not advance us towards our goals and objectives, then we will always feel frustrated and stressed, because we will not have enough time left for what would get us to where we need to be to feel successful. If you have unnecessary things in your life, you will have to spend time on their maintenance and upkeep, which is time taken away from the necessary and important things. Or, if you neglect them, this will be another stress to carry around. So whichever way you look at it, you do not want unnecessary things!

Clearing out

A wise spiritual healer I know says that you must always clear to move forwards. Often the reason we can't move on, or feel blocked, is that we have not thought enough about clearing out, or eliminating, some of the clutter and excess baggage we carry, both in our outer life and our inner thoughts and feelings.

Becoming clear is a great way to release ourselves from stress, and we are talking about being clear about what you want in your life, and what you do not want, or need, any longer. But, of course, it is impossible to have more of what you want if your agenda is still crammed full with a great deal of what you don't want!

Take an overview of your life and imagine you are about to have a huge springclean! How would you go about it? It is certainly not usual to get so carried away with the impulse to springclean that we throw everything out and buy all our possessions anew. That would be ridiculous. However, deciding to let go of some of the stuff we have been hanging onto can feel such a relief! It makes you feel so much lighter. And once you let some things go, you can appreciate the value of the good and necessary things. But when you are cluttered up, you can't see anything clearly, you just feel overloaded by everything – even the good things.

Therefore, to become more in control of our own agendas the first thing that is necessary is to give ourselves permission to jettison all the stuff that is not really of our choosing; things that we are not really too comfortable about, but which we have somehow been persuaded that we *should* (there's that word again!) accommodate. We have to get rid of the 'stuff' that is bogging us down to no avail. Once you've cleared some space, you can then think about what you'd really like to have there, or whether perhaps you simply enjoy having the space.

It's important to remember that it is, after all, *your* agenda, and so you are entitled to be in charge of it! It is also important to work out just what stops you from doing what you want to do. When you are being true to yourself, rather than complying with some idea of what you 'should' do – or be – much stress is released. I came across a releasing little message recently on a calendar aimed at 'Women Who Do Too Much!' It said:

> 'We are not really asked to live anyone else's life. All we have to do is live our own, and that seems to be quite enough, indeed.'

Of course, it is an obvious statement, but just seeing it stated baldly like that made me feel suddenly freer. And I started to think about how much of other people's lives encroach on our own; how much time we perhaps spend thinking, or gossiping, about other people's problems, which won't make a bit of difference to them and certainly won't take us nearer to our own goals! How often do we agree to meet up with people in whom we are not terribly interested? Or how much time do we spend thinking about famous personalities in the news and everyone else we encounter through the media, whom we don't even know and will probably never meet? How much time and attention do we give to thinking about other people's successes or failures, what others should, or should not, do? How much emotion is spent on worrying about friends and family or others' opinions and so on. This is energy and time taken away from our own lives. So just take a moment to say to yourself:

> 'I only have to live my life.'

And repeat it regularly a number of times every day. Then give up trying to live other people's lives for them!

Reviewing your agenda – 1

Now spend a little time mentally reviewing your agenda. Try to get in touch with the things that you really do not want to do or the attitudes you project that are not really your own or the beliefs you pretend to subscribe to which perhaps get you into situations you'd rather not be in. Make a list of these things that you want to be rid of: the baggage that is weighing you down. You may wish to organise it in two columns, one headed

'Outer Agenda' for things in your outer life that you would like to jettison, and the other headed 'Inner Stuff' for your attitudes, thoughts, fears, beliefs that trip you up and keep you un-free. Alternatively, you may just have one continuous list. Then mentally sideline them every day. The way to do this is:

- Look at the list, or the two columns, a number of times a day and as you focus on each item say to yourself:

> *'This is not part of me. This is not part of my life.'*

- Have the list beside you on the seat of the car as you drive to work or as you return home after the school run. Each time you stop at a traffic light, glance at one item on your list and repeat the sentences as above:

> *'This is not part of me. This is not part of my life.'*

- Or mentally repeat this exercise on your journey into work by train, bus or bicycle, or while out walking the dog. Choose the most urgent to focus on first and gradually work down the list.

- Do the same at regular break times during the day: at a coffee break, at lunchtime, at a tea break, on the train on the way home or in the bus or car, in the supermarket queue or waiting to go into the cinema – anywhere you suddenly have a little space, just affirm to yourself what is not you and what you do not want! Just repeat:

> *'This is not part of me. This is not part of my life.'*

- Especially go through the exercise last thing at night before you go to sleep, so that the thoughts are carried into your subconscious mind as you fall asleep.

You have to say the phrases in the present tense to convince your subconscious mind that the statements are true right now – even though they are not. Because if you say them in the future tense, for example, 'This will not be part of me for much longer,' your subconscious cannot know when the message is going to apply, which will confuse it, and so it will be disregarded. You have to start believing it right now.

The frequent repetition of this exercise will create strong new neural pathways in your brain and will convince your subconscious mind of the truth in the statements. You will then discover that your external behaviour begins to alter in a way that more truly demonstrates who you are and what you want. Once you start to alter your inner conditioning many of these things will just take care of themselves. When your inner attitude changes a lot of things will just fall away, or you will simply lose interest in the things that were not really necessary. For example:

- You may suddenly realise that you have stopped thinking you have to agree with everyone, and you may find yourself saying things like, 'Actually I don't agree with that. I see it differently. . .', where previously you would not have wanted to upset friends by disagreeing with them, but would secretly be angry with yourself for not expressing your true feelings, thereby creating internal stress for yourself.
- You may suddenly stop being ashamed of your rather battered old car. You may find yourself thinking that it actually doesn't matter if you don't have the latest BMW, as you know you are respected for who you are, by the people who really count, and not for what you have. You may realise that your car is a reflection of your bank balance, not your essential self, and that a funky old car is actually more individual anyway! Phew. . . What a lot of stress you can release!

- You may find that you don't have the same interest in reading gossip columns in the press, or watching trivial television programmes, and this will give you more time.
- You may discover that certain tasks you undertook before suddenly seem unnecessary, and that you find a way to get round them, or to delegate them, or simply eliminate them from your schedule. It is amazing how you can change things once you have made up your mind – and informed it of the fact! Persevere, and see how well it works.

Reviewing your agenda – 2

Another way to work with your agenda is to look at all those areas of your life at this moment that you wish you had more control over. Write them down as they come to you, no matter if they seem silly or unrealistic. Just put them down on paper – in a list, in a circle, in a pattern, inside balloons – whatever feels right; it does not matter how you do it, only that you *do* do it.

Now look at each of these areas individually and ask yourself, 'Where is the "should", in this? Am I caught up in someone else's "should" or even in my own ideas of how I "should" behave or how I "should" look?' 'Shoulds' and 'oughts' are thoughts which imply someone else's control, and make us feel heavy, burdened and weighed down. If the answer is, 'Yes, I am caught up in some kind of "should"', replace the 'I should' with 'I do not want' and see how the situation changes. Then, after the 'I do not want,' say to yourself, 'But I want . . .' and finish the sentence. You will most probably feel very uncomfortable with the notion of 'I want' but just go along with it for a while, to get the flavour of what 'could be'. This means, what could be the possibility for your life if you were to give yourself what you really want. Even if this appears unrealistic, given all the usual constraints of ordinary life, just go with it for a while. This will give you the sense of how you might make some adjustments that could leave you less stressed, less distressed and more in control of your agenda.

This exercise can reveal things about what is dictating your agenda. For instance, you might be saying to yourself (and others), 'I should stay in my rather boring job, because it pays well,' but realise that you feel angry and bitter at how much time you are wasting doing a job that does not really inspire you. So you then say, 'I do not want to go on with this tedious job!' Next you add, 'But I want . . .' and it may be, 'But I want to work part-time, so that I can build up my graphics portfolio to help me get work I really enjoy and which uses more of my talents.' You could then decide that you will manage to live on a reduced income for a while, so that you can go for greater rewards later on. This way you have been honest with yourself about what you want and you have faced up to the price of having less money, for the gain of doing what makes you happy and releases your stress.

Or another situation might be that you are caught up in the thought, 'I should help my friend move house.' But you recognise that you feel resentful about the time you would have to spend on this, when you are already feeling overloaded with all the things you need to get done in your own life. You also recognise that this is a recurring pattern: always trying to help others at your own expense. Then you think, 'I do not want to help with the move.' However, your next thought is, 'But I want to be a good friend, it is important for me to be kind and supportive.' So what you could do is to tell your friend honestly that you do not have time to help with the house move, but you want to take him/her out to dinner on the evening of the move, to relieve their stress. This means you can still achieve the desire of being helpful and supportive, but in your own way – in the way that does not compromise you. Sometimes it's a question of just looking a little more deeply into the problem and finding that there is a way of doing what you want, which also manages to take care of the 'should' in a creative way.

On a more mundane level, you may be saying to yourself, 'I should clean the house,' then you substitute 'should' with 'I do not want,' so you are then saying, 'I do not want to clean the house.' Next you add, 'But I want . . .' You may say, 'But I want a clean house.' In that case, you have two choices: clean the house yourself or find someone else to clean it. If you then decide that you cannot afford to pay anyone to do the cleaning, you could decide to focus on the result you want – a clean environment – and so you could then decide that you 'want' to do the cleaning because it would give you the result you want. When you change the 'I should' into 'I want' it has a different energy to it: it feels lighter and freer. However, you might have said, 'But I want to work on the book I am writing . . . go to the cinema . . . meet a friend for a drink . . . paint the bedroom.' If one of those 'I wants' was judged by you to be a better use of your time, that would take you nearer to one of your life goals, then you could give up the 'I should' and make an adult decision to spend your time in the most productive way for you, thereby releasing yourself from guilt and stress.

In other words, creating your own agenda means becoming more conscious, more aware of taking responsibility for your decisions, and believing in your right to do so! If you can decide that the 'should' part of your agenda is actually something you 'want' to do, this, of course, will make a huge difference to your stress levels. When you are doing what you 'want' to do, you eliminate the tension, the resentment, the lack of commitment and the potential damage to your health. You stop feeling like the underdog or the victim of things outside your control. Sometimes just affirming to yourself that you 'want' to do certain things that you *have* to do can make all the difference between feeling weighed down and over-burdened, or feeling confident, effective and in control. One way to achieve this is to focus on what will be the *result* of doing what you 'should', and quite often – as in the example above – we actually 'want' the result. So if you focus your attention on the 'want', then you may find it easier to take the action that will get you to the result. If, of course, you don't see any advantage in the result of doing what you 'should' do, then what is the point of doing it?

A quick rule of thumb, which I often use, is to ask myself if what I am doing, or planning to do, is essential for my health, my wealth or my happiness. If it is not going to benefit me in any of those areas, then maybe it is just a waste of my time. This is not always applicable – but it gives you a starting point if you're confused about anything you're thinking about doing, or anything you want to give up.

Another way to control your agenda is to substitute the word 'should' with the word 'could'. So instead of saying to yourself 'I should do so and so,' you say 'I could do it.' This implies choice and your own autonomous control. The word 'could' means that you can if you want to, but you don't have to – there is no coercion. So you are nobody's victim, you are not manipulated and you can choose what you wish to aspire to be, to do or to have.

Prioritising your agenda

A wise elderly lady I used to know said that she always divided the demands of her life into three categories:

a. Things which could be done.
b. Things which should be done.
c. Things which must be done.

Then she said that she tackled the 'c' category first, the 'b' category next, and lastly the things in 'a'. Well, that is one way of doing it. And it is certainly a good, straightforward strategy for prioritising your tasks.

However, taking this idea further into the arena of releasing your stress and taking more control of your agenda, my suggestion is that you make three lists under the headings of the above categories, but fill in each list with the things that 'could', 'should' and 'must' be done to make you happier and more fulfilled – in other words, things for you. What you 'could' do for you, what you 'should' do for you, and what you 'must' do for you: but only you, not for anyone or anything else! And take them seriously! This is important, because it is so often the case that we do not take our own needs, and wants, seriously enough, or we relegate ourselves to the end of the list with an unspoken proviso, '. . . if there's any time left,' and usually there isn't! And the reason, of course, is not prioritising ourselves highly enough. Do work on writing these lists, as they will be very revealing. Whether you act on them is up to you. But if you do not find yourself actioning any of it, please, at least, ask yourself why.

Give yourself what you want

My own feeling is that one of the 'musts' for feeling more in control of our agenda is to put into it enough of what we 'want' to do at a deep level, not just what we need to do. What I mean here is something that is connected to your values. If we spend too much of our limited time on tasks and activities that are not terribly meaningful to us in terms of our value hierarchy, we become stale and un-energised.

Even today, I think women are conditioned (perhaps there is some genetic programming also involved) to put aside their own desires and focus more on the needs of others. It is difficult to get women to say what they *want*, although they will more easily talk about their needs, by which they can justify – albeit unconsciously – getting what they want. Men, however, are usually much more comfortable with doing what they want. I always encourage my women clients to develop that more masculine drive within them-selves that says, 'I want!' and doesn't feel guilty about wanting, but feels important enough to be able to have what it wants. Wanting is connected to the will and the active principle; needing has more of a passive quality. Of course, they are both valid – but wants are often more fun! Also, the deeper desires within us are real and create havoc in our lives if they are never heeded. Depression is often due to suppressing important 'wants', and disruptive behaviour in children can be traced to the same cause, because some of our 'wants' are expressions of who we truly are.

I suggest you flip through your diary – or possibly last year's – and register your feelings as you look at what you've been doing.

- What would you like less of?
- What would you like to see there more often?
- Why are you not putting the things you want into your schedule?

Now simply give yourself permission to create your agenda as you'd like it to be – to have more of what you want. Start on this by putting into your diary just one thing each week that you want more of. It may be more 'time off from mundane tasks' – well, take it! You could code it in, if that would make you feel less guilty. For example, put: lunch M.E. or put your initials, or a code name for yourself, and treat it in the same way as you would a lunch date with one of the most important people in your life. For you *can* be one of the most important people in your life, and you deserve to be taken out to lunch by you! Or for a walk in the park or to the movies or an art exhibition, or whatever you really want to do. Don't cancel it if something else 'important' turns up; be firm that you must honour the commitment to yourself. Treat yourself with awe and respect, and don't dare cancel! The other thing can be fitted in at another time. After all, if you had an urgent appointment with your dentist and that other 'important' event arose, you wouldn't automatically cancel the dentist, would you? Well, your wants are as important as toothache! In fact, they are an ache of a kind – and you must ease them; it's your responsibility.

Once you get used to this weekly treat, put two or three more special events for you into your week. You could code them S.E. (Special Event) and write: meeting with S.E. Or block out certain periods that are just for you – to use as you desire when the time arrives. You will actually do everything else so much more effectively for having had a little more of what you really want, for you will not be carrying so much resentment. Giving yourself time to engage with whatever you really want will probably mean you'll still get everything else done, because you'll work at it with more ease and happiness.

A client of mine had a very strong-minded mother, who at ninety years of age was still running her own hairdressing business. She came from a working-class background, was very religious, had a powerful sense of the work ethic and was highly suspicious of leisure. She expected her son to think the same. For many years he worked obsessively at building up his own business, until he became exhausted from overwork, which was when he came to see me. He felt guilty if he took time off to enjoy himself, but I managed to persuade him that taking holidays was not sinful, it re-energised you to work more productively on your return. Equally, taking time out for fun and pleasure would help, not hinder, his work life. He has now reorganised his agenda to give himself more time for himself, and is a happier and healthier man. His mother rings every Sunday for a chat, and if he is not there she asks accusingly what he has been doing. Happily, he no longer feels guilty about looking after his own needs and wants, but doesn't want to upset his mother, so he tells her he was in church, although he is usually out having lunch and enjoying himself. This satisfies her, for she cannot change her ways, and stops any quarrels or tensions between them which would be pointless at this stage in their relationship. Actually, he is looking after his mother, as well as himself. Now this may appear deceitful, but you don't have to burden others with your guilty feelings about doing what you want to do. If my client had 'confessed' truthfully to his mother, it would have meant that he was still playing the child role looking to his parent for approval or permission. As adults we ultimately only have to answer to ourselves. If you know you need to change your agenda in certain ways, then the only permission you need is your own.

I am not exactly encouraging indulgence; it is more a matter of recognising that there is no parent figure or fairy godmother out there somewhere, who is going to make sure that our lives are as we want them. We have to do it for ourselves, and believe we can!

The reason most people don't create the lives they really want, is because they don't think they can. What I am saying is just give it a little try, start with small things and see how possible it is. When we really believe that something can happen, it does. I'm not suggesting that you can become a millionaire overnight, or a genius, or anything fantastic. I am simply saying you can dictate the content of your agenda more than you may think. The more you do this, the more you will believe you can. You will strengthen your will-power and your belief in it.

It takes a certain amount of self-discipline to action this necessary concept, and discipline may have negative associations for you with school, teachers and other authority figures. However, self-discipline by its very nature eliminates the need for outside authorities, so it actually frees you up. In fact, this can be one of the first steps in offloading baggage. Rid yourself of other people's authority voices in your head and replace them with just one – your own!

Offload unnecessary baggage

Often we carry on with old ways of behaving, or old images of ourselves which are not appropriate any longer, and these may be some of the things that have to go. You may have needed certain adaptations at one time, in order to cope, but you may have outgrown them. The old coping mechanisms or beliefs and attitudes can become handicaps when they have gone past their 'use by' date.

For example, a client of mine felt that she was not connecting properly with the people around her; she said her relationships were unfulfilling and unrewarding, and that people did not react to her as she wished they would. She asked me, 'Is there something I am doing that is causing this problem – do I need to change something in my behaviour?' I suggested that she live with the question for a while and attempt to observe herself as objectively as possible. So she pondered on this; she watched herself carefully when with her friends and listened more acutely to what she was saying. She began to realise that she was not actually presenting herself to the outside world in a manner that reflected how she felt inside. She was making too many jokes, and appearing to treat trivially issues that were in fact extremely important to her. She was not taking herself seriously and so others did not either. But this was second nature to her; she had always experienced difficulty believing in herself and in her right to have views and opinions, expecting to be ridiculed, or dismissed. She was the youngest child with four older brothers who had paid little attention to her during her childhood, except to laugh at her when she played the fool. This became the way she gained their attention and a glimmer of admiration. Thus she got into the habit of playing the court jester, making the trivialising joke or dismissive statement first in order to protect herself from rejection. She took on the 'joker' role with school friends as well, for it made her popular; but as time went by it became unfulfilling to be seen only as a clown. Once she understood more clearly how this adapted behaviour had originated she began to feel freed up, and very tentatively started to express more honestly what she really thought or felt, courageously risking dissent or dismissal from others, although mostly it didn't come. Gradually her confidence and belief in herself grew. But importantly, her relationships felt more real and meaningful and, to her great surprise, she found people listening with respect and, in fact, taking her seriously. She did not lose her sense of humour, but stopped using it as a barrier – almost a weapon – to hold people at bay. She learnt how to honour and reveal other sides of her character as well. This demonstrates how something that works at one time in our life isn't necessarily successful forever, and may need rethinking. My client is now more relaxed and happy than ever before in her life, for she has been able to throw away a protective habit that was no longer protecting her but imprisoning her, by cutting her off from others.

So give some thought to what you could jettison into the metaphorical trashcan or shredder. Whether outgrown inner attitudes, or clutter in your outer life, some shedding will free you up to feel more in control.

What to offload

Ask yourself:

- What would give you just so much relief not to have to deal with anymore, or have around you any longer?

- What do you wish you never had to see again?
- What would you love to get rid of in yourself?

Close your eyes and call up in your imagination the sort of things that make you unhappy. (If you like, write them all down in a list or as a diagram.) Next, imagine yourself setting fire to them and watching them dissolve into tiny ashes; see them floating off into the sky, away above the chimney tops. Make a pact with yourself that you really are going to do something about these things. You are truly going to ensure that you let go of a lot of the stuff that bothers you, however much you might hear an inner voice (or an outer one) telling you that you can't do this! You decide!

Of course not everything has to go. It is your life, and only you can decide what is good, or bad, for you. Some things should remain with us for our entire life if they are valuable to us, for whatever reason – even if others may consider them clutter or junk. I think I have made it clear enough in what I have said previously that I do not subscribe to the opinion that if you have not worn, or used, something in the past twelve months then it should be chucked out. That's much too formulaic. We are each unique and have to make the specific decisions for ourselves, honouring our own feelings. I think the best way to judge this is at the feeling level: when we listen to our feelings they rarely lie

If certain things are making you feel uncomfortable or unhappy – whether they are possessions past their 'use by' date which are cluttering up your life, relationships that do not fulfill you (in spite of trying hard at them), activities you no longer enjoy or traits in yourself that do not serve you positively – you may want to consider parting company from them and no longer giving them your valuable time and energy.

Often, of course, we discover wonderful treasures in the process of clearing out our clutter. A client of mine had a treasured collection of letters from special people, ranging over many years of her life, which she said affirmed her life and gave her pleasure to read through from time to time – especially if she felt down or depressed. She told me of the day she was looking through a box of letters which she thought were from her ex-husband, but discovered they were actually from her to him! He had obviously kept them, and when they separated they must have been mistakenly put with her things, so they went with the wrong person. But did they? She was suffering from rather low self-esteem on the day she decided to look through this box, and she thought that his letters might hold some clues about their relationship split and where she'd gone wrong. But what happened as she read through the letters she had written was that she was shown a picture of someone rather interesting, witty and bright, and she couldn't find the evidence of her inadequacy, awfulness or badness, that she felt convinced was the truth. Instead, the truth about her 'OK-ness' was in front of her. They were treasures indeed for her, although someone else might consider them clutter. So we have to become clear and strong in ourselves about what is clutter and doesn't help, and what is supportive and necessary, even though it may be taking up space.

If I know that certain possessions like books, clothes, or some of the 'objets' I have inherited make me feel good and uplift me, then no one is going to persuade me I should get rid of them. Those things are my friends, they cheer me up on a regular basis, make me smile to myself, and therefore serve a totally valuable purpose. However, if some of the things in your house, in your outer life or even in your friends make you feel upset and stressed you may need to decide to take a deep breath and say 'goodbye' to them. Don't do this in a negative state of mind: feel love for whatever you are letting go, wish it well, but affirm to yourself that you are moving on. Then feel the relief, feel the release.

To sum this up rather simplistically, a neat little yardstick to apply to your agenda is:

> *'If it doesn't make you happy, chuck it! If it makes you happy, keep it!'*

Make space for your mind

One of the most important needs in our overfilled agendas is to find space and rest for our minds. It is far more tiring to use your mind than your body. The reason children can be so active from morning till dusk – exhausting for adults – is because they do not have so much 'stuff' in their minds.

As we all know, one of today's big problems is excess of information; there is so much to absorb, and so many new things coming at us every day, that it is hard not to feel overwhelmed mentally. Even though much of it may be very exciting and interesting, too much of anything – no matter how good – just adds up to overload. News, views and innovation incessantly pouring out at us from various sources is extremely demanding of our mental resources. No wonder people's nervous systems are on overdrive!

Mental strain and jittery nerves result from being too much focused on the outer world: the world of sense impressions. It is fatiguing to the mind to be constantly focused outwards; the brain needs to focus inwardly as well, in a rhythmical, balanced way. This, of course, is why we need to sleep regularly. But even during the waking day we still need to rest and balance the mind. It is for this reason that meditation is practised in India and much of the East. It gives the balance to sense-orientated impressions, putting the mind into another mode, with brain waves often slowed down, which can be as refreshing as a night's sleep.

Just as the body needs variety of activity, so does the brain. We have imaginations and memory, and if we don't use them sufficiently they atrophy. Most people do not spend enough time looking inwards: reflecting on things, thinking, imagining. This is something we have de-emphasised in the West, as we have come to value the outer world more highly than the inner world. Although, if you think about it, so much of what we focus on outwardly is actually a product of the inner world: the imagination!

A nice saying I encountered recently is:

'Profound pauses cannot happen unless I pause.'

So another space-clearing exercise is to make some special space for your mind and your nerves – give them a break from working overtime, all the time! Put regular slots into your timetable for giving your mind space, calm and peace. Think of it as de-toxing the mind. It is important to remember that we have to be responsible for feeding our mind – just as much as our body – with good quality input. It doesn't necessarily have to take long; you could just take five or ten minutes to stare out of the window and rest your mind on the sky, trees or whatever you see. Or close your eyes for a few minutes and imagine a white sheet of paper – this is very calming – think of it as a kind of mind 'fast'. Just let whatever you have been concentrating on slip out of your mind for a moment or two. You can't actually think about nothing (unless you are a highly developed yogi) but if you imagine a blank sheet of white paper that will get you near to emptying your mind. You probably won't be able to hold the image for long, but that doesn't matter – a few seconds, a number of times a day, will make a difference.

When you have longer, put aside say half an hour to listen to some soothing music; memories are often triggered by music, which takes us on a journey inside. Equally take your mind on refreshing journeys in the outside world: take a walk around the block or through the park or some beautiful garden square and be nourished by the magical sights of nature. Bathe your mind regularly with other uplifting images like paintings, sculpture, beautiful architecture, but especially give yourself time to look inwards, and to visualise internally. Wander through your imagination and dream, as this is refreshing and balancing.

Visualisation

A quote I like is:

> 'Dreaming is not limited to the unreal. Dreaming is stretching the real beyond the limits of the present.'

In fact, it is only by dreaming, visualising, imagining that we can create the future. One really inspiring inner activity I recommend is to imagine your life as you would really like it to be. Inwardly picture everything as clearly and completely as you can. For, if we do not have a vision for what we would like to create in our outer life, then it is very difficult to make it come true. But when we create a clear picture of what we are aiming for, it is amazing how much easier it becomes to achieve it. So this could be the way for you to begin spending more time on the inner dimension.

Practice the visualisation techniques I give you throughout the book, and begin to create your own inner landscape of wonderful and soothing places. Also, sometimes visualise just one object or symbol that calms you, like a lighted candle, a cross, a lake or a white rose. By varying the inner pictures you give yourself a sort of inner work-out, and strengthen your ability to focus on whatever you decide. Also, when you observe pictures or create picture images in your mind, you switch from the logical, left hemisphere of the brain into the right, creative and holistic side. This is uplifting and makes you feel mentally better balanced.

Meditation

Meditation is a very important antidote to our busy, frantic society and you may want to learn this practice. There are many forms and methods of meditation. Some focus on concentrating the mind, in a similar manner to the visualisation techniques I have suggested above, although the practitioner is usually given a word, or sound, to repeat inwardly and which has no association with their everyday life. This is intended to lift them to a higher plane of consciousness, to a transcendent state. Other meditations may focus on movement or chanting. The method you choose will depend on your personal inclination and your goals. You could join a group or you will find a number of instruction books available in bookstores. (There is more on meditation in Chapter 11.)

Resting the mind

A friend of mine, who has a very high-powered position in television, always takes at least twenty minutes at lunchtime – half an hour if possible – to shut herself away and be quiet. Her staff are instructed not to disturb her, just as they would be if she was in an important meeting. Of course, she *is* in an important meeting – with herself! She lies on the floor of her office and practices some relaxation techniques and then takes herself on a guided daydream to a beautiful place in the countryside. When she re-emerges she is ready to deal with the second half of the day; she is refreshed and has realigned herself.

It is vitally important to rest the nervous system. It has been proved in many research studies that those who take regular 'mind breaks' have greater energy and stamina than those who take regular coffee breaks!

If you think about it, what is it that actually goes to sleep when we sleep? Is it our heart or our liver or kidneys? No, all of our organs continue to work when we are asleep. It is the nervous system that sleeps, that cuts off from the world. This is absolutely essential if we are to function in a rational, effective way during the day. We all know how it feels not to have enough sleep – you cannot think straight. The mind needs a rest from sense impressions, transmitted through the nervous system, and in sleep we are protected from outer sense impressions. That is really what sleep is, it's like turning the computer off.

The more help and rest we give the mind and nervous system – not just by switching off in sleep, at night, but by switching inwards from time to time during our day, the better the mind will work when we return to focus on the outside world.

Also practice saying to yourself, 'Just because it's out there, doesn't mean it has to be in here,' – that is, in your mind and nervous system. Avoid cluttering up the internal you. One way is to have regular space clearing sessions such as I have outlined above, and another way to help yourself is to create files on your PC, or actual physical wallet files, of all the new and exciting places, items, thoughts, sayings and so on that you come across and feel excited by, so that you do not have to overload your mind. I have a file called 'Resources File' for just such a collection and one of my new mottos is, 'Write it down!' This is partly because my memory is not what it was, but also I am adhering to my philosophy of not cluttering my mind.

Einstein is reported to have said that he never attempted to remember people's telephone numbers – he maintained they were written down somewhere and he never cluttered his mind with anything unnecessary. You may think that memorising certain phone numbers *is* necessary, but the practices of a genius should not be ignored, so I would advise that you simply apply the general principle in a way that is appropriate for you. Taking the advice of people who are successful is always sensible life management.

In fact, watching and learning from successful people, or people you admire, is a marvellous way to improve your performance in life. If someone is functioning in a stress-free manner and coping well with life's demands, then try to observe very carefully how they do it: how they structure their time, how they prioritise their tasks, how they deal with others, and so on. As children we learn everything by imitation – by copying the people around us – and I see no shame in continuing to do this throughout adult life. There will always be someone ahead of us, who has cracked the code to certain of life's riddles, and from whom we can learn. Just take time to observe very attentively what it is they are doing that you are not. Instead of wasting energy envying someone else, use your energy to consider what it is that makes them more successful and then copy them! This is another aspect of offloading your burdens;

or rather, transforming your burdens into their polar opposite. So, don't envy, but emulate!

Don't put yourself down either, by admiring someone too much. A wonderful quote sent to me by a friend recently sums this up:

> *'We become whole by withdrawing our projections and owning our own talents and skills.'*

I think that is such a lovely twist on the usual connotation of projections, which are generally seen as being those negative, dark parts of ourselves that we do not acknowledge, but ascribe to others. The thought that what we admire in someone else could be our own hitherto unseen talents, skills or qualities is delightfully uplifting, and not usually considered. I have always believed this is what happens in hero-worship – we give away our own hero. When we adulate pop-stars we neglect to express the 'star' within ourselves. Carl Jung, in fact, stated many years ago that whatever we admire in another, we possess within ourselves. For if we did not contain that particular quality or ability, he said, we would not be able to recognise it in someone else. So whatever you admire about somebody, just start to develop that potential in yourself – it's there lying dormant or just escaping your notice.

Let go of the negative self-talk. Answer it back! You don't have to take critical remarks from anybody – not even yourself! I have a voice inside that I call Carp. It carps on about this and that not being right, and I just tell it – in a most loving way, of course – to shut up! Sometimes I converse a little more intelligently with it, explaining very patiently that things are not always perfect and that I certainly am not. Moreover, I should not be expected to be perfect, for nobody is, and I think we should all allow each other a few frailties and inadequacies. That's how I keep this inner critic at a distance – I just don't buy everything it comes up with. We have to take responsibility for not allowing our inner critics to undermine us, so that we can get on with the task of becoming all that we were intended to be.

A lovely saying I have pinned up in my hallway from Eleanor Roosevelt is:

'No one can make you feel inferior without your consent.'

This is exactly right. Not even you yourself! So withhold your consent!

Create clear boundaries

One other very important aspect of taking more control of our agendas and our lives is to be clear about our boundaries. To set limits and then be firm about sticking to them. This stops us feeling blown about all over the place or subject to other people's agendas. In the next chapter I address the very important need to say 'No!' We can all find it hard to utter this word in certain circumstances so turn to the next page to read my suggestions for how to go about setting up firm boundaries and safe space.

5

The 'Positive No'

Unclear boundaries cause a great deal of stress, both for ourselves and other people. We are often afraid to say 'No', for fear of offending or upsetting others and we then get pushed beyond our limits or find ourselves doing things we really didn't want to do or we allow others to encroach on our space and time. How often has this happened to you? How often have you wished you'd said 'No'?

Saying 'No' is a way of protecting yourself. This little word can help you to create more of what you want in your life, so in that sense it is one of the most useful words in your vocabulary. This is why I want to put before you the notion of the 'Positive No'. We often fear to use it, or feel upset when it is used towards us, simply because we give it a negative connotation. But if we could see 'No' as a positive utterance then we might see its creative advantages. It is positive because it makes things clear and gives us the power not to be pushed around by other people.

'No' asserts your ego – your sense of self – and can be used to free you up, if you believe in your right to use this little word. It is very simple. It is a way of declaring where your limits lie. We can make things extraordinarily complicated for ourselves, but this simple word is all you need. It is quite amazing where we can end up by simply failing to say 'No'. Just reflect on the undesirable things you have brought upon yourself by saying 'Yes' or 'Maybe' when you should have said 'No'.

It is important to recognise that while someone else may experience your 'No' as a negative impact, when seen from your own position it is acutely positive, and treats you with the respect and consideration you deserve. It defends your rights and sensibilities. A recent quote I came across says it well:

> *'When I say no to a request for my time, I am not going away from that person, I am going towards myself.'*

Actually, when we put down boundaries, we are making life easier for everyone: we are providing clarity. When we do not recognise and acknowledge our limits, we often end up carrying a great deal of resentment, which is uncomfortable and gives us baggage we don't need. But we must take responsibility for not having said 'No', for not having put down the boundary, and thereby causing ourselves unnecessary stress. If you don't tell someone where the limits lie, you can't really blame them for not knowing! This is about acknowledging genuine limits, not selfishness or excuses. We all have limits to our energy, our patience, our ability to absorb information and to the amount of time available in each day, week, month or year. The problem is that when we don't acknowledge them we often end up not only feeling angry and put-upon – often upsetting others as well – but not being who we could be. If we give our time to people or things that don't really need us, or allow our energy to be leached, we have insufficient of either for our own achievements. The most successful people are very careful about how they spend their hours and how they use their energy.

Using the 'Positive No' enables you: it is not resistant or drawing you away from life. It frees you to say 'Yes' to the things that will take you forward, that will enable you to achieve your desired goals, and not get side-tracked down a cul-de-sac.

I think women have more of a problem with setting clear

boundaries than men because it is a woman's nature to be more diffuse. Women can usually handle a number of tasks at the same time, whereas men are happier dealing with one thing at a time, in a linear fashion. This means men are often more focused and single-minded in their endeavours, which makes it easier for them to say 'No' to distractions or sidetracks. And it often means that women take on far too much! However, a male friend of mine, who is a very enlightened business consultant and author, is currently having a big problem with this issue. He is constantly swamped with requests to give talks, or to meet with individuals and groups to discuss his ideas and visions, and can't resist saying 'Yes'. He has a very generous nature and finds himself endlessly agreeing to en-counters he later regrets or discovers are a complete waste of time from his point of view, with people merely wanting to draw on his inspiration and energy, with very little return to him. He has just put a sticker on his telephone which reads: 'Say "No!".'

A part of the problem can be that we have been brought up to believe that we must consider others first, and not be selfish; this was certainly true in the case of my friend. This conditioning, coupled with a compassionate nature, as well as being a Virgo sun sign with Mars in Cancer (for the astrologers among you), meant that he genuinely felt for others and wanted to be of service. But always saying 'Yes' when sometimes he should have said 'No' became undermining, as he couldn't give himself enough of what he really needed. Eventually, quite late in life, he learnt that to be selfish in the right way results in being more true to yourself: more self-like or self-ish. Being true to yourself generally causes you to feel more at one with yourself. When you are being true to yourself you are also able to be more true to others. Remember the lines from Hamlet (Act 1: Scene 3):

> 'This above all − to thine own self be true,
> And it must follow, as the night the day,
> Thou canst not then be false to any man.'

So honour your 'self' by being clear about where you stand. Take yourself seriously – if you don't, others won't. This does not mean you have to be rude or unkind, you just have to be clear – in your own mind first and then in your interactions with others. We are talking about time boundaries as well as space boundaries. If you know you have a time limit in a meeting, for instance, then state it at the outset so there is no confusion. Other people will often want to push you beyond your stated limit, but as you have already told them what time the meeting has to end you should feel no guilt in sticking to this. One of the best ways to avoid others' attempts to provoke guilt in you, is to appear very surprised that they have not taken your initial statement seriously. Never justify – just stick to your message that this is the time you have to leave. A friend of mine always arrives at my house with a huge clock which he heaves out of his bag and places somewhere extremely visible. He then tells me how long he can stay and when the clock reaches that time, he rises and leaves! Simple! I am sometimes a little dismayed that he can cut short whatever interesting topic we are focused on, but I have to say that I respect his resolve.

Establishing boundaries

To establish clear boundaries, it is not always necessary to actually say 'No'. Sometimes you just have to think it. But you then have to act it in your body language. In other words, it is no good thinking 'No' and acting 'Yes'. We often give confusing signals.

Another friend tends to do this. She has very weak boundaries and I often end up having to create them for her. At the end of an evening she will keep saying she must go but she never does! She remains sitting where she is rather than getting up and moving her body towards the door. So she is saying that she has reached a boundary but not acting on it. This can be not only confusing to others but irritating. It can be an hour, or even two, after the first protestations that she should leave, until she finally gets up and does so. When I am very tired I find this extremely annoying, because she is not telling the truth, and it makes me feel as if she is dallying with me – not taking me seriously. If you make a statement that needs to be followed up by action, but you don't take the action, it leaves everyone confused as to what exactly is going on! If this happens – as it frequently can between friends or business colleagues – you have to decide that you will take the action to firm up the boundary limit. Therefore with my friend, after the second or third announcement of her imminent departure, I usually stand up and say something like, 'Shall I get your coat?' or, 'Where did you put your bag?' or even, 'Yes, I am feeling very tired, I think I need to get to bed.' If she still doesn't move I open the door of the room we are in and walk slowly towards the front door. Or, I might get up and go to the bathroom, come back and remain standing – signalling that the cosy chat is over. What I am actually signalling is that I am ready for my space to revert to me and so now I am taking control of putting down the boundary. I left it to her for quite a long time, out of consideration and politeness, but now I've reached my limit – I'm saying this particular evening is ending and I don't feel guilty about it. We each have a right to be able to control our space and time in this way. Sometimes both parties may be vacillating and neither is really doing what they want to do. When this happens you can feel the energy seeping away, because each person is denying their inner drive to go for what they really want and therefore their energy is being suppressed; it feels very uninspiring.

In a work context, if you wish to end a meeting you can use the same tactics. Get up out of your chair, and say something like, 'Well, it has been very interesting to meet you, and I hope we can be in touch again soon. Thank you for coming to see me.' If the other person does not respond by standing up also, and maybe tries to continue the conversation, you should walk slowly towards the door, repeating the message in slightly different words, and then just stand silently, waiting, near the door. This should have the desired effect. Of course, you can actually say, 'I must stop now, as I have another meeting in five minutes,' or something along those lines. But if someone refuses to take their cue and tries to keep you engaged in conversation, don't feed it. In other words, after they have spoken, don't add anything, apart from perhaps a smile and a nod of your head. Just hold your ground and refuse to be sidetracked. If that doesn't work, you could try the 'broken record technique', which is simply to repeat, again and again, your last statement. So you would say, 'I must stop now, I have another meeting in five minutes,' as many times as necessary. It is very effective.

Whether you genuinely have another meeting or not doesn't matter, what does matter is that you have the right to control your time and space and put down boundaries. You are not a dispensing machine and you do not have to be endlessly available to all and sundry. You may simply want some time to yourself, and that is perfectly valid. The important point being that *you* should consider it valid to honour your genuine need and not feel guilty about it. So much of the time we feel guilty if we are not giving someone else what they seem to need. But 'seem' is the relevant word here. You never truly know what someone else needs – you may think their need is greater than yours but it is just possible that this is not the case. You do, however, know how desperate, or reasonable, are your own needs at any time. These should be honoured as often as possible. By following this logic, when you receive satisfaction of your needs on a fairly regular basis, you will have plenty to give to others when necessary.

If you want to say 'No', but think you should be saying 'Yes', it is often because you think or feel that 'No' is somehow rude or offensive. The way round this one is to say 'No' with a 'Yes' voice! Practise this by saying 'Yes' to yourself when you're alone, then say 'No' in exactly the same way. The tone of your voice has the most important impact. It has been discovered in research studies that our tone conveys the message much more powerfully than our words. So practice saying 'No' with an uplift at the end. Usually it is said in a very final tone, with a forceful and abrupt ending. Try saying it with a slightly lingering ending. Then combine the lingering sound with the uplifting, or positive, tone. This can never sound offensive, or aggressive. But it is still 'No'! In fact, it is the 'Positive No'. The important point is that you should not make people feel they are being rejected or given the brush-off. It is not *against* them – it is *for* you.

As I said above, this is a way of protecting yourself from the stress of being pushed into doing things you don't really want to do, or which are wasting your time and energy, and not helping you to achieve your objectives. It gives you the key to stepping out of the victim role, and into taking control and responsibility for creating your life the way you want it to be.

Visualising boundaries

Other ways of putting your boundaries in place can be achieved symbolically, or imaginatively. An exercise I frequently introduce to clients who are feeling over-run by someone, or intruded upon, is to visualise a protective barrier between themselves and the other person. This is your secret way of saying 'No'. Some people have used a piece of clothing – for example, a cloak which they visualise putting around their body to keep the other person out. One client always put on her imaginary blue cloak when she went to visit her extremely demanding invalid aunt; this made her feel protected from the pathetic but aggressive comments intended to make her feel guilty for not giving more of her time. She was a very sensitive young woman, who genuinely felt a great deal of compassion for her aunt, but simply could not give her any more time as she was a single parent with a small child to look after as well as a demanding job. So putting her boundary in place meant that she could give a certain amount of care and affection, but not be sucked into colluding with the older woman's complaints, which would have meant visiting for longer and neglecting essential aspects of her own life.

Another client recently visualised a bubble around herself, which kept others at a distance and protected her from their negative 'vibes'. She felt safe when she was inside her bubble. She is a social worker and often receives abuse from people she is trying to help or from those from whom she is trying to protect others. She really needs her bubble!

A recent divorcee used a perspex shield to protect her heart and solar plexus from too much emotional contamination or emotional blackmail. And a male client said he could visualise a giant sieve around himself, which allowed the finer particles through but kept out the gross, unrefined stuff coming at him from others, or from the general environment. This made him feel more in control, and more peaceful about his life situation.

A woman who felt extremely vulnerable visualised a concrete wall between herself and the world, but on her side she created a gentle stream babbling around the bottom of the wall and a beautiful garden. In the wall itself she had narrow slits like in fortress castles, which she could see through, but at which she also had powerful guns positioned in case she should need to blast anyone!

Some items can be used literally to provide a protective barrier in certain circumstances. A colleague of mine, who also worked in this way with her clients, had a very difficult relationship with her mother. She was continually hurt by her mother's criticisms and barbed remarks. She loved her mother, and really didn't want to stop seeing her, but decided she had to do something to protect herself. So she took to wearing a wide belt with a huge silver buckle whenever she visited. She visualised to herself that the buckle was a protective shield, and that the hurtful things her mother said just bounced off it, like bullets ricocheting off a tin can. This really helped her not to react inwardly quite so intensely, as she used her buckle to help her prevent the painful words from penetrating.

I often suggest to my clients that they hold something in front of their solar plexus region (in front of your stomach, where emotion is felt most acutely) if they have to be in situations which make them nervous or distressed in some way. For example, if they have to attend an important interview or meeting with their boss. What I recommend is that they carry a newspaper, a briefcase or possibly a handbag and that they then position the item across their solar plexus region and imagine it is a protective barrier that nothing can penetrate; a sort of shield that they are safe behind. Or, you can simply clasp your hands together – not too tightly – preferably, just put one on top of the other, and hold them in front of your stomach imagining they are your shield, giving you the protection you need.

Establishing boundaries and 'Safe Space'

It is vital for releasing stress and for our general wellbeing that we have space for ourselves, and to feel that we can control our space. You may allow others in, but the point is that you have the control and the right to say 'No'. Anyone else can only enter your space when you say so. If this is impossible to achieve in the outer world it can be achieved through visualisation. You can create the perfect space for yourself in your imagination, and go there whenever you have some time alone. This can be wonderfully affirming of your inner life and your own autonomy: in other words, of your right to withdraw from the outside world whenever you choose, into a beautiful interior world. As I have already said, I actually think it is very important that we recognise the reality of our inner world, and feel comfortable and peaceful within ourselves. The more you become the creator of beautiful thoughts and images inside yourself the less you will feel a stranger there. This, of course, is the aim of some forms of meditation: to create peace within our minds and find a refuge there or, as I call it, an inner sanctuary.

But it is also important to create some kind of sanctuary in the outer world as well – a space that belongs to you and no one else, if you possibly can. Somewhere you can go to be alone and in peace, or in any state you want at that moment. It may be you want to play a particular kind of music or read or watch a video or just sleep. You may live alone and therefore it will not be too difficult to organise this. But if you have a family or a partner, try to have one place that feels like your own 'safe space' – or your stress-free zone. If it can be your own room, that is ideal, but even a part of a room, or a desk that belongs to you and which no one is allowed to invade without your invitation, would give you that necessary personal safe space.

A client had moved into his girlfriend's house, after separating from his wife, and was feeling very destabilised and not too comfortable. He wondered why he was not feeling happier. We did a visualisation exercise and he asked himself where exactly in his mind, body or emotions was he experiencing the discomfort. Eventually it dawned on him that he had no sense of really belonging in the new house. I asked him what might give him that feeling of belonging, and he realised that he greatly missed his desk from his former home: it had felt like 'his inviolate territory'. This realisation was very important to my client and he went out the next day and bought himself a desk! It was the beginning of really feeling 'at home' in his girlfriend's house: the desk was 'his space'. As time went by he also took some control of other aspects of the space in which he now lived, how it was ordered and decorated, and they became true partners. But he needed his desk to give him his sense of selfhood. It was almost symbolic: a little like a child when away from home needing to take a special toy which connects them to their safe space at home, or a comfort blanket which makes them feel safe.

Your own personal space could also be a space of time, so that, for instance, you take half an hour, or an hour, when you withdraw into your bedroom to meditate, visualise, or practice your relaxation routine; and this is respected as inviolate by the rest of your household. You are not allowed to be disturbed, except in an emergency, for this is your 'sacred' space. Equally, you could instigate this kind of 'time space' in your daily routine at your office, as does my friend the television producer I mentioned in Chapter 4, who takes time in the middle of the day to be alone, firmly believing in her right to give herself this space. Or, if you do not have a private office, you could put space for you into your timetable each week by going to sit quietly in a church, or even in a park or garden square, at lunchtime. Or, possibly just take time to have lunch alone, so that you can go into your own interior space. Even if you are reading during that time, you are still connecting with your inner self of thoughts and feelings, and this takes you to another place. When you return you will feel refreshed simply because of the change of focus.

Affirm to yourself that you have the right to set limits and establish boundaries, and to protect them from being trampled down by others. Feeling you have control of your space, and time, will release you from a great amount of inner stress and should give you a feeling of greater ease generally. But the only way you achieve this is by using the 'Positive No'!

6

Let's talk about your body

The science

In many ways this is the most important chapter in the book because it sets out the physiological reactions to, and consequences of, stress. When we can control these reactions we have one of the major keys to controlling our physical health. For no matter how intelligent we may be, or how many cognitive, sporting or artistic skills we acquire, or how much wisdom, if we cannot protect our bodies we may end up the most accomplished patient in the hospital ward! Few people realise the damage they may be causing their body when they go into the stress reaction, and it has always surprised me that we are not taught more about the internal workings of the body, in terms of looking after it, while we're at school.

The stress response

The stress response is actually a wonderful, and necessary, set of internal reactions programmed into the body, designed to save our life; they automatically go into action when the mind perceives some kind of danger or threat. The stress response is also called the 'Fight or Flight' response and, as the name implies, the internal changes it brings about have the purpose of making you stronger to fight or flee your way out of physical danger. For example; if you suddenly realised your house was on fire, you would not sit down with your partner and have a conversation about it, or stand around thinking what to do – you would get out! You would move without thinking. Or, suppose you stepped absent-mindedly into the road, and suddenly saw a car coming towards you; you would not stand there trying to work out the speed of the car and how long you had before it hit you! You would find yourself back on the pavement before you had time to think. An automatic response, that overrides your logical, frontal brain, takes over. You simply take the appropriate action without even thinking what the appropriate action should be. Many incidents have been reported of people lifting cars, fallen trees, or other impossibly heavy objects off someone, thereby saving their life. This is all the work of the 'Fight or Flight' response. It turns you into a 'super-human being', giving you great strength and speed. It takes over when logical, rational thought is not the answer. It is something that has been programmed into you, to help you in an emergency, and on which you can absolutely rely. So this aspect of it is extremely positive and desirable; it must not be seen as the enemy, for many lives have been saved, and accidents prevented, due to its workings, which I'll explain in more detail below.

The trouble is that the mind often causes this reaction to be triggered when there is really no life-threatening situation, because so many of today's threats and difficulties are not physically dangerous but rather present a threat to our emotions, self-esteem or intellectual wellbeing, and the stress response does not help us cope with those. In fact, it can hamper our ability to function in the face of these kinds of threats, and this is where it turns negative. What the mind perceives may well be extreme, but if it is not an actual threat to life all the physical changes that start occurring are a little like revving a car engine when the car is stationary. It's not good for the car, and not good for the body either! If we're not going to run or fight, or exert ourselves physically, then there is not much point having all the engines blasting away, it simply wears us out, and worse. When all the body's survival resources are being mobilised as a result of receiving danger signals from the brain – possibly countless times a day – this puts a great strain on many internal systems. The eventual outcome of this may be permanent damage or a malfunctioning in some organs or systems. Changes that were only intended to be temporary can become long-term, like raised blood pressure, increased sugar output, reduced fertility, and much more, which then become a health problem.

The 'Fight or Flight' response is an emergency response, meant to be switched on for short periods only – just long enough to get you out of danger. Many people, however, are in this state for too much of the time – without realising it – because they feel threatened, angry or wound up by numerous everyday situations. Even over-excitement can produce it. This is a natural and useful response in the right context, but when a physical reaction is not appropriate, you have to learn to switch it off. For, not only is it exhausting to your body, but it also puts the body into a very unbalanced state. Certain systems necessary to help you go into overdrive are activated, while others that have no part to play in the emergency are switched off or put into a state of reduced function.

I should now like to outline for you the changes that take place in the 'Fight or Flight' response – the stress response – for if you understand what is actually happening inside your body, it will be easier to understand the methods I shall then describe for switching off the response, and putting the body back to normal functioning. Understanding will encourage and motivate you to practise these. In my view, it is usually because people don't see the point that they resist introducing changes into their lifestyle. Also, I am a firm believer in the saying, 'Knowledge conquers fear,' so here is the 'knowledge': the science.

What happens to the body

Raised blood pressure and the pounding heart

The heart rate speeds up in order to carry more blood, more quickly, to the large muscles that would be needed for quick flight or fighting an aggressor, and to supply the lungs with extra oxygen. This is, of course, highly desirable to make you stronger in an emergency, as discussed above, but can be worrying and annoying at other times – for example, if you have woken in the night and need to get back to sleep, or if someone upsets you, or you are engaged in a heated argument. A rapid heartbeat is not, in itself, dangerous to your health, but because it induces raised blood pressure, it is undesirable for any length of time. If the response is activated too often, it can lead to permanently high blood pressure, which can then lead to a stroke. It is especially bad news to have high blood pressure if you also have high levels of cholesterol in your blood and deposits in your arteries. This puts your heart under strain, and any extra stress could push you into the danger zone.

Angry people tend to suffer from high blood pressure more often than those who can remain calm in the face of pressures and problems; if you know this is a particular problem for you, it might be beneficial to your health (as well as your relationships!) to attend an anger management course. In my experience, suppressed anger is the most lethal of all. In my counselling work I have found that many clients who suffer from high blood pressure are unaware they are angry; they discover in the course of therapy that they are suppressing deeply buried anger from the past, usually from childhood, which is creating inner tensions and sapping their vitality. Once they can acknowledge and face those dangerous feelings, they feel a sense of release and relief, which invariably has a positive effect on the blood pressure readings. If you feel this could apply to you, I would strongly urge you to seek out a counsellor, or psychotherapist, with whom you feel safe and comfortable, so that you can work on the anger issue. In addition, if your family has a history of heart problems, or poor lifestyle habits, have regular check-ups with your doctor.

Blood clots more readily

Extra blood clotting factors are released from the spleen, to prevent excessive bleeding were you to be wounded. Again, necessary in a real battle or physical accident, but not helpful in the day-to-day mental and emotional battles of ordinary life. To have thick, sticky blood circulating round your body much of the time can cause the formation of blood clots, and puts extra pressure on the heart. The additional work involved in pumping the blood can cause energy levels to decline, making you feel fatigued, and can also cause raised blood pressure. If you know you go into the stress response frequently, make sure that you drink plenty of water – at least two pints, or one and a half litres per day. This helps to thin your blood; and is healthy for your body in any circumstances. (If you are taking any medication for an existing condition, check first with your doctor about the implications of increased water consumption, especially if you suffer from epilepsy.) Also, learn the relaxation techniques that follow in the next chapter, which put the body back to normal and control all these responses.

Hormonal and chemical changes occur

Extra cholesterol is produced from the liver when in the stress response, to supply extra energy. Therefore, keep a careful watch on your diet when stress levels are high, and do not add to your body's supplies of cholesterol; in fact, try to reduce your intake of fats and dairy products so as not to overload your blood and induce fatty deposits in your blood vessels, especially your coronary arteries.

Extra adrenalin is pumped into the system to keep the 'Fight or Flight' response going, and to enhance physical strength. Adrenalin makes you feel 'high' and 'supercharged', and many people are hooked on this artificial energy, which can cause eventual burnout; it also seems to diminish the capacity for clear, rational thinking. Once adrenalin has been kicked into your body you have to be patient until it has run its course. Try not to get agitated about this hyper feeling, as you will simply pump more adrenalin into your system. I always say, 'Try not to get into a state about being in a state!', especially if you have woken in the middle of the night, or you will keep the hyper-arousal running. If, for example, your neighbours are saying noisy farewells to their guests, and much slamming of car doors and honking of horns is taking place, do not get wound up and angry, justified though this may be, or you will still be lying there fuming when everyone next door is happily snoring! You must say to yourself in these circumstances, 'Ah well, I have been woken up – never mind, I'll soon get back to sleep, no problem.' You have to fool your mind that it is nothing to bother about, and that way you remain calm and peaceful, and will soon slip back into sleep. Just lie, or sit, calmly and practice relaxing all your muscles, and the arousal will soon calm down. Remember, it is how the mind perceives something that makes all the difference, and in order to protect your health, your sleep or even your sanity, sometimes you have to pretend to yourself that annoying situations really do not bother you.

Extra cortisone is also released from the adrenal glands as a protection against inflammation or allergic reactions. This may be helpful in the short term, but the long-term effect can suppress the immune system and so reduce resistance to illness. Healing, which depends on inflammation, is also impaired, and ulcers can result from excessive cortisone secretion. Another of the corticosteroid hormones secreted under stress, cortisol, interferes with the liver's ability to regulate fats and, together with adrenalin, turns off the long-term building projects of the body, such as tissue repair, growth and bone recalcification, in favour of the short-term gain of saving your life. As you will realise, long-term health is being sacrificed whenever we switch on the stress response, which is why it is important not to use it unnecessarily.

There is an increased output of endorphin – the 'feel good' hormone – which is a very powerful painkiller, and accounts for people not feeling the pain of a wound until some time after an accident or fight or whatever. However, if the stress response is activated for long periods without respite, it seems that the levels of endorphin are diminished, which may explain why emotional stress can cause us to avoid physical stress, as we instinctively know our threshold to physical pain is lowered.

The supply of sugar increases

The liver releases greater amounts of sugar than normal to provide extra short-term energy to fight or flee from danger. If this sugar is used up in some kind of physical exertion all will be well, but if it is not, it places a huge demand on the pancreas for extra insulin to facilitate uptake by the body's cells. This can result in breakdown or malfunction of the pancreas, and some doctors believe that diabetes can be aggravated, or even caused, by prolonged stress responses. It is very important, therefore, not to indulge in foods with high sugar content at stressful times – unless you are having to make extra physical effort – for the body is already coping with an excess of sugar.

Excessive sweating occurs

Sweating is the body's cooling mechanism and when faced with any threat this response is heightened to prevent you overheating during a battle, or in running for your life. Of course, in a social or business context this reaction is simply embarrassing, which adds to one's stress. Try reassuring yourself that your sweaty hands and glowing face could, one day, save your life! This might make you smile to yourself and so relax you, thereby switching off the unwanted adaptation.

Skin turns ghostly white

The colour drains away from the face because of a reduction in the blood supply to the surface blood vessels as it is needed elsewhere, and also to protect us from bleeding too heavily from a surface wound.

The senses are heightened

We talk about people bristling with anger or indignation, and this is literally what happens. When we are alarmed all the hairs on the body stand on end just like a cat's, and although you can't see this reaction, you can sometimes feel a tingling sensation in your skin, especially up the back of your neck. This is a leftover response from primitive days, which is intended to increase your body bulk and make you look more frightening to an opponent or enemy. However, it is not much use in the modern context, when the enemy may be a traffic jam, a delayed train, a cashpoint machine that refuses to function or your PC that has crashed for the fifth time that day – or all of these! Whatever the cause, this response makes you particularly sensitive to your closest environment, which is why, when you are feeling stressed, you often don't want other people too close, and you feel hypersensitive – for instance, you may perhaps react more aggressively than usual if someone accidentally bumps into you.

In fact, all the senses of the body become sharper and more intensely tuned in times of stress, producing increased clarity and focus – a sense of 'aliveness' – the pleasure of which attracts people to engage in high risk sports and other dangerous pursuits. It is also what causes people to produce their best work when under pressure. This heightened alertness, however, although ideal for dealing with a true emergency or a dangerous situation, cannot be maintained for long periods without respite. After prolonged stress, the senses seem to burn out and become dulled, so that reaction rates slow down. There can also be a tendency to 'switch off' from the outer world, and this can be mistaken for depression, when it is actually exhaustion from hyper-arousal; what is then needed is rest from too much stimulation for a while, until you feel restored. Try to be aware if your reactions have slowed down after a prolonged period of stress, and don't be afraid to admit it to yourself. It could be dangerous in situations where it is essential to be alert, such as when driving any vehicle, or using machinery, or any other potentially perilous activity, like climbing a ladder doing house repairs, or even crossing the road, so just take extra care and extra time for things.

This reaction of intense alertness, and its rebound consequence of extreme burnout is what was referred to as 'shell shock' during both world wars: the most effective treatment for it was prolonged rest away from any pressures. In my experience, a so-called 'nervous breakdown' is often due to the same cause: an overloading of the nervous system and the senses, inducing chronic hyper-arousal which prevents the individual from ever switching off sufficiently – leading inevitably to complete exhaustion and inability to function. Again, a long period of rest and the absence of demands or pressures may produce respite and cure, and in my opinion, this should be the first line of treatment before drugs or psychiatric methods are introduced. So the possibility of complete exhaustion should be considered when a clinician is presented with patients suffering from nervous conditions. If you feel on the edge of nervous collapse – that you cannot cope with anything – give yourself a rest cure; just do very little apart from eating and sleeping for a week or two, and see if that restores you.

A reduction in libido occurs

The body is, in fact, extremely pragmatic, so that when facing some kind of threat to its life, it switches off, or reduces output, in all the systems not needed for the struggle to stay alive. Therefore, its logic is that if you are in a life-threatening situation this is not the moment to procreate or indulge in sexual pleasure, so it shuts down, either completely or partially, all the sexual systems and focuses its resources to where they will be needed most to save your life. In other words, sex is superfluous in a situation of great physical danger. As a result of this logic you will experience a decrease in libido – in both desire and performance – and decreased fertility when you are in the stress response. There is reduced production of the sex hormones: testosterone in men and progesterone in women.

This can be the cause of many women's failure to conceive, when medical tests have shown there is nothing physically wrong. It can be the reason for impotence in men, or premature ejaculation. It is also frequently the underlying cause of a decrease in sexual desire – all of which, of course, can be immensely upsetting when not understood or explained sufficiently well by your doctor. Many doctors will advise a worried couple to learn to relax and take a holiday together, reassuring them that all will be well. This is good advice, because all methods of relaxation will switch off the stress response, allowing the body to return to normal functioning – as long as it is true relaxation, and not simply a diversionary activity, like going to the pub or playing competitive sport, which still leaves the individuals tense and wound up. Relaxation usually needs to be taught by an experienced teacher, for, although it is a skill that we're born with, most people in the developed world have lost the ability to call upon this natural reflex.

If you can get away, the more relaxed atmosphere of a holiday will usually work wonders, generally introducing greater opportunity, as well as increased inclination, for love-making, provided the couple are not emotionally wound up and tense about their unsuccessful sex life. Being away from the pressures and strains of everyday life should automatically bring about increased physical relaxation, which will return the sex hormones to normal levels. The effects of relaxation on fertility can be widely observed in reports of the many couples who conceive when they stop trying – sometimes after they have adopted a baby, or after they have just resigned themselves to not being parents. However, all advice to go on holiday and learn to relax is not going to be comforting to people who think there is something seriously wrong with them, unless the thinking behind it is explained fully. This is why it is so important to understand these stress responses.

If any of the above is a problem for you and/or your partner, try to be patient – don't allow it to cause more worry and stress or to damage the relationship. Recognise that it is most probably the result of physical stress responses, rather than a sign that you are no longer attractive to, or sexually attracted by, your mate. Heed the advice above and learn the relaxation techniques I describe in the next chapter.

If you are unable to go away, then take mini-holidays at home. Unplug the telephone for the weekend or leave your answering machine to take all calls. Stock up on your favourite food and wine, beer, champagne or whatever you like most. Rent a number of videos, put your feet up and indulge yourselves unashamedly for two whole days. Take time to read to each other, maybe a favourite childhood story or a poem, or make up stories – one of you starting it, then the other taking over, and alternating like this until you arrive at the ending. Then put on music and dance together (like you used to perhaps when you first met – why do we stop dancing after about the age of 25?). Leave all mundane tasks until next weekend and 'play'. Take long, foam-filled baths – preferably together – take it in turns to give each other a soothing massage with sensual oils, have picnics in bed – and see what happens! Just enjoy yourselves utterly and completely for forty-eight hours. You'll probably feel 10 years younger on Monday morning, and this could be the beginning of a whole new way of life! It could certainly be the beginning of family life. If you don't have a permanent partner, just apply the advice in a singular way. See Chapter 9 for more about being on holiday all the time.

The digestive system shuts down

Once again, if the body has received messages from the brain that you are facing a serious threat, it will prioritise against eating a meal in favour of saving your life: resulting in the complete, or partial, shut down of the entire digestive system. This is why your mouth goes dry and it is difficult to swallow when you are anxious or frightened; also, you generally lose your appetite, as it would be inappropriate to eat when the system isn't working. The body's logic is that if someone was pointing a gun at you, for instance, you wouldn't be likely to say, 'Hang on a minute, I've got to eat my lunch!' So, forget lunch or tea or dinner if you're stressed, because you won't digest it very well. The digestive juices are needed elsewhere, and so is the blood normally employed in supplying the stomach; it is diverted away to the large muscles of the body, to give you that extra speed and strength. The blood vessels to the stomach contract, allowing little blood through, and this can be the cause of stomach ulcers, for without sufficient blood supply the lining of the stomach begins to die. The layers beneath cannot cope with the concentrated digestive acids, and begin to burn, hence the pain. Prior to this extreme state, you are likely to experience other digestive disorders such as indigestion, nausea or cramps.

Irritable bowel syndrome is another consequence of this response, due in part to the fact that your food has not been properly digested and broken down, firstly in the mouth and then in the stomach, and so gives the bowel too much work to do. This causes excessive contraction of the muscles in the walls of the intestines, which stretches the sensory nerve endings; function is impaired and pain is experienced.

Therefore, it is highly undesirable to attempt to eat when you are worked up in some way, as you will not be able to digest your food properly. If you are in a stressed state, sit quietly for a few moments, practise relaxing and breathing rhythmically and slowly (see Chapter 7 for correct breathing), and give your body time to return to normal functioning. This was originally the reason for saying a grace before meals – to introduce a moment of calm, and create a space in which to unwind and let go of the preceding activity. What wisdom! It might be sensible to re-introduce this tradition; in fact, I have friends who do so for the sake of their children, as it quietens them down before they eat.

At the very least, try always to sit quietly for a moment before you begin to eat, try not to eat 'on the run' and try not to have arguments during meals. This latter point is especially important with regard to children; if they become upset at mealtimes, they simply cannot eat or digest their food fully. So try to avoid battles about eating, and create a calm, happy atmosphere before, and during, mealtimes. Do not scold children if they refuse to eat when they are upset, for they are instinctively right – they genuinely cannot.

Breathing becomes rapid and shallow

This change facilitates a quick exchange of gases – oxygen and carbon dioxide – which increases the performance of the lungs. This is useful when you have to exert yourself, but not if you are sitting still, perhaps tensed up in a state of anxiety, anger or hurt. The altered breathing rhythm can cause panic attacks due to hyper-ventilation: over-breathing for the activity you are engaged in. If you were running or fighting or exerting yourself physically in any other way, then your oxygen requirement would be greater than if you were sitting still. But if you breathe in more oxygen than your body can use up, the excess stays in your blood, and causes the symptoms often experienced in panic attacks. These are dizziness or light-headedness – as if you are about to faint or as if floating through fog or with your head full of cotton wool – tingling in the hands and fingers and sometimes in the toes, a restricted feeling across the chest or a choking feeling in the throat. The reason is too much oxygen in your blood and too little carbon dioxide. This altered breathing rhythm can become a permanent habit, leading to frequent panic attacks and/or constant uncomfortable symptoms like the ones mentioned above. In this case, the individual never feels really well, or fully functioning, and is always frightened that the panic attacks will overwhelm them and possibly cause their death from asphyxia. This won't happen, but the sensations are very unpleasant. It is important that sufferers of panic attacks are taught how to bring their breathing down to their diaphragm and breathe normally again as nature intended. Some people get into a bad habit of holding their breath when under strain and this can also cause similar symptoms. Many sufferers of panic attacks are advised to carry a brown paper bag with them and to breathe into it at the first sign of symptoms. This is good advice, as they will then inhale the carbon dioxide they have just exhaled into the paper bag, which restores the balance of oxygen and carbon dioxide in their blood, and gradually the symptoms will subside. (Obviously, don't breathe into a plastic bag, otherwise you could suffocate!)

It is important to recognise when your breathing has become shallow and altered from its normal rhythm. Learning to control and calm your breathing is one of the most important skills you can acquire for release of stress and upset of all kinds. It is a physiological fact that you cannot feel anxious and breathe calmly at the same time, so learning to breathe correctly gives you the key for controlling your emotional responses. If I could only teach one stress-reduction technique, I would teach correct, abdominal breathing, for it is so effective in calming the whole body and mind. Some yoga disciplines teach very undesirable breathing techniques, which can lead to hyperventilation, due to blowing away too much carbon dioxide. You should never completely empty the lungs of carbon dioxide. (See Chapter 7 for more on this and correct breathing technique.)

Muscles tense for action

It is mostly the large muscles that tense up in the stress response: those that would be needed for the action of running or fighting, like the muscles in your legs and upper arms, the ones that clench your fists and the muscles in your diaphragm, or solar plexus, to protect against a blow. The shoulder muscles will hunch up, and the buttock muscles may tighten, as might the muscles in the soles of your feet and your toes. Another instinctive reaction is to frown and clench your teeth – to make you look fierce to an opponent! Most people report feeling tension first in their shoulders and then in their arms and hands. But if you try to become aware of your entire body when you feel anxious or threatened or wound up, you will notice all the other areas of tension also. Often people are not aware that they clench their teeth much of the time until it is pointed out to them – many do this in their sleep without realising it until their dentist remarks that they are grinding their teeth away. The same applies to frowning – people are often unaware of it. But frowning tightens a band of muscles around the head and can cause headaches.

Tension is tiring. It requires considerable use of energy to hold muscles in a contracted state: just try holding your arm out in front of you for about ten minutes and see how tiring it is – your muscles will ache from the effort. Chronically tense people are generally chronically tired; they are using so much energy to no avail. Letting go of the tension – relaxing and loosening up – will remove the fatigue and free up that energy for living. I see people walking down the street with clenched fists and arms held tightly into the sides of their body as if they were afraid their arms would fall off if they let go or let them swing loosely. Or people sitting with tightly crossed legs – impeding their circulation – and with arms folded tensely across their chest, pushing their shoulders up into a hunched position and constricting their breathing. Such a terrible waste of effort!

Furthermore, it is the tension in muscles that sends the alarm messages to the brain via your nerves signalling the need to switch on the 'Fight or Flight' response. So whenever you have excessive tension in any part of your body, not only are you wearing yourself out but you are also activating the stress response and many, if not all, of the above changes. You can, therefore, see why it is so desirable to relax as much as possible and not use more tension than necessary for any task. Habitually tense people risk having permanently raised blood pressure, suppressed immune systems, reduced fertility and all the other emergency adaptations I have described.

It is not surprising that a researcher into the stress syndrome recently stated:

> *'How we live affects how long we live.'*

If you rush about in an aggressive manner getting angry and wound up at the drop of a hat, you are constantly putting your whole system under extreme strain. Naturally enough, if you face a truly life-threatening situation – as in any of the many parts of the world where civil wars are raging, it is almost impossible to relax; to slip easily each night into unguarded sleep, or to connect inwardly with joy, harmony and calm. But many of us behave as if we are in the front lines of a war zone in everyday life, getting so worked up about the smallest things. Just taking some time to consider what it might be like to find yourself caught in the cross-fire of warring groups – to risk a bullet every time you go to the shops – could put our stresses into perspective, and we might stop reacting to someone taking our parking space as if we are fighting for our lives! That outcome really doesn't matter. Why shorten your life for it? Why burn out over all those little irritations – like someone cutting in front of you on the road? Why not just smile and wave him or her on? Possibly chuckling to yourself about the number of times you've done the same to someone else, instead of reacting as if they'd just murdered your mother!

In the next chapter I am going to give you ways of controlling the stress response, or discharging it. I shall also introduce you to some simple but effective loosening movements for unwinding your tensions, some ways of relaxing more in everyday living, and finally I shall give you a deep relaxation routine to restore you completely.

Physical exertion can also be a good way to let off steam, and sometimes it is necessary to go into action to use up the stress chemicals sloshing round your body. So if you find yourself getting really wound up, with all systems racing, and you can't let go and relax, then go for a run, walk vigorously or run up and down a few flights of stairs. If none of that is possible in the circumstances, go to the cloakroom and jump up and down on the spot and practice some air-boxing, or tackle some physically strenuous job. But after you have let off steam and discharged the pent-up energy, do practice some of the unwinding and relaxation exercises in the next chapter. It is always important to relax and unwind eventually, to put your body back into neutral, back to normal. So, turn to the next chapter for how to do this.

7

Just relax . . .

As I have said a number of times, relaxing your body is the way to switch off the stress response and one of the most important skills to acquire for your stress release tool-kit. It is impossible to be wound up and physically relaxed at the same time. So taking the time to learn how to relax your main muscle groups, and developing the awareness that tells you when you have tensed up again, is one of the simplest but most effective ways of keeping yourself in a good state.

Relaxation instantly releases you, mentally as well as physically, but sadly, many people have forgotten how to incorporate it sufficiently into their daily lives. It is easy in today's world to feel that you cannot take time off to relax, that you must be focused and active at all times, or you'll never get it all done. However, if you relieve the pressure regularly by giving yourself some relaxation breaks, then you can take much more pressure in the long term and, ultimately, achieve the success you desire rather than collapsing from burnout, or any of the other health problems related to stress, with the consequence of being forced to take a long break you don't really want! As you will have gathered from the previous chapter, resting and relaxing your body means less wear and tear on your internal organs because you are releasing the body from the stress responses and in a state of deep relaxation you are actively assisting the body's repair mechanisms.

First of all, you can help yourself on a day to day basis by being more aware of how much tension you use for all your usual tasks. Then just try to use a little less effort for everything, make all your movements more relaxed and less tense, whatever you are doing. Apart from taking time out to relax deeply, you can help your body by being more relaxed in all your movements throughout the day.

Many people are wound up tight all the time, without being aware of it: holding their shoulders hunched up for no apparent reason or clenching their hands tightly. Remember that tension will send signals of distress to your brain that switch on the emergency response: the 'Fight or Flight' response. So try to use only the minimum amount of tension (or tightness) necessary for the task in hand; do not put excessive effort into it. I see so many friends and colleagues using too much energy all the time without recognising what they are doing to their internal organs; even clenching your fists for a few minutes can send your blood pressure up! So imagine what is happening when you hold the telephone too tightly all morning, when you grip the paper you're reading with all your might, when you have your arms tightly folded across your chest for an hour or two during a meeting or your hands clasped tightly together all evening watching TV, or when you tense up too tight doing DIY or gardening, gripping the paintbrush or garden trowel more tightly than necessary. Experiment with how much effort you need for your various tasks. Then watch yourself in your daily actions and try to become more aware of how much effort you are putting in. Is it the right amount, or is it too much?

For example:

- How tightly do you hold the steering wheel when you are driving?
- Do you have the right amount of tension in your grip to control the wheel, or are you using more effort than required?
- Do you grip it so tightly that your knuckles turn white?
- Do you clench your teeth? We don't need the muscles in our jaw

to drive a car, or to read a report, listen attentively or think! However, we often have them tightly held, and many other unnecessary muscle groups as well. This is very tiring and wastes your energy.

- How much effort do you use in: washing up, vacuuming, ironing, making your bed, chopping vegetables, washing yourself or shaving?
- How much effort do you use opening doors or carrying your shopping?
- How tightly do you hold the telephone. Do you grip it as if it were a 10-ton weight?
- How tightly do you hold the knife to butter, or cut, a slice of bread? Or your knife and fork when eating?
- How many muscles do you use when you are keying into your computer. Are you clenching the muscles in your toes, thighs, stomach or forehead? How many unnecessary muscle groups are you using which could remain relaxed?
- How tightly do you hold your pen to control it across the page. Does tightening your grip help you to write faster, or make you more creative? Of course not, it merely tires you more quickly than necessary, makes your hand ache and switches on the stress responses.
- Do you hunch your shoulders when sitting at a keyboard, when playing a musical instrument or painting – or just most of the time!
- Do you frown when concentrating or when playing games like golf, tennis, board or computer games?

Do you see what I am getting at? All of this extra tension is frittering away your valuable energy and winding you up internally. Check what is happening in your body right now as you read this. Is there unnecessary tension in your stomach, your feet, your toes, your legs, your neck, your shoulders, your arms, your hands and your jaw? Keep checking yourself many times each day, so that you gradually become more aware of which parts of your body you habitually hold on to or hold in tension.

Pace yourself: balance doing and non-doing

Relaxation and tension are two opposite states, and ideally we need a balance of each. Total relaxation happens when your muscles are doing nothing, completely still and resting. Further on in this chapter I shall give you a routine for deep relaxation, to use whenever you have run out of energy or when you feel anxious and wound up. In this state the body can replenish itself more completely and calm down all the racing systems, as well as the anxious mind. It allows the body to restore correct internal balance and homeostasis. For example, medical research indicates that the immune system functions far more effectively when we are in a state of deep relaxation, that is with muscles totally resting and with all body systems slowed down. Other repair and regeneration processes have been found to be enhanced when we are deeply relaxed.

There are two metabolic processes in the body: the catabolic and the anabolic. The catabolic process is the wearing down, and using up, of our bodily systems, and is in action when we are. The anabolic is the opposite process which is responsible for maintenance, repair and up-building, and is brought into play when we sleep, meditate, rest or relax. It is obviously important that we spend sufficient time in the anabolic state.

You could think of it like this: When we are not relaxing, we use ourselves up; when we relax, we build ourselves up.

Tense muscles use energy and give off a waste product. This waste is acid in nature, and when we continually push ourselves beyond the point of natural fatigue the result can be too much acid in our system; this can be the cause of aching muscles and joints. The antidote is rest and relaxation. A relaxed muscle is resting, conserving energy and causing no waste, and will switch the metabolism into anabolic mode. But, as I said above, being more relaxed in all your movements, even whilst working, can help you to save energy and therefore you will have more available to you for longer periods. You will also feel healthier due to having a more alkaline interior state. Try to apply maximum relaxation and minimum tension to everyday tasks. In the words of Plato:

> *'Maximum work with the least effort equals grace.'*

Tension overdraws your energy account

Tension often becomes a bad habit that creeps up on you gradually, until you literally cannot relax because you have lost the natural ability to let go. Many people run their energy accounts on permanent overdraft, wasting their precious energy by being tense when they think they are doing nothing (and when they could be relaxing). For instance, when watching television, sitting reading, in the cinema or even when they are asleep they are tensing their muscles. Therefore, the sleep does not restore their energy loss. So habitually tense people are usually chronically tired people, always overdrawing on their body's supplies of fuel and oxygen, i.e. their energy supplies.

Think of relaxation and tension as two ends of a pole balanced on a central point – like this:

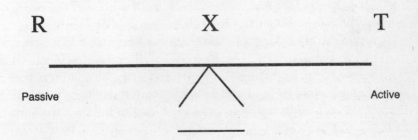

Too much activity and tension is exhausting, and too much relaxation and passivity can cause feelings of lifelessness, stagnation, depression or powerlessness, which are just as stressful as too much pressure. Having too little to do can be as much of a problem as having too much to do. Ideally, we all need a creative balance of both ends of the pole. This does not necessarily mean an equal amount of time at each end, because this is not always possible; but if you have been at the active, tense end for long unrelieved periods and have become severely depleted of energy, then you will probably need an equally long period at the resting, passive end to restore you and put the balance right. However, people do recover their vitality at different rates, so it is always important to listen to your body and heed the messages it is sending to you.

You may worry that you will never get back into activity if you relax, and certainly sometimes, if you are very tired, you may feel more exhausted after you have relaxed for a while, but this is simply because you are getting in touch with what is actually your true state at that time, and it indicates that in fact you need more rest. Generally, after a spell of relaxation you will feel released from tension, re-energised and refreshed. However, even if you do not have enough to do and you are not suffering from too much activity, you could still be suffering from being wound up and tense too much of the time – often through the frustration of insufficient occupation. In this case you will need to balance things by taking more exercise and finding ways to introduce more activity into your day. The loosening and stretching routine outlined later in this chapter will give you a starting point. The best formula is a little of one side of the pole, balanced frequently with a little of the other, to keep the balance from tipping too far towards one extreme.

It may be worth taking a lesson from the heart: an organ that is designed to last a lifetime. The heart is an 'all or nothing' organ: it is either working, or resting – it beats and rests, or contracts and relaxes continuously – and the healthy heart rests slightly longer than it works. I think this is an example for us to follow if we want to last a lifetime too!

Tension is tiring

Tension is, of course, necessary to perform any action. When we function efficiently we use the right amount of tension for the job in hand, but when we are feeling stressed or under pressure we usually tense up tighter and tighter in an effort to try and cope more effectively. Up to a certain point, extra tension can improve performance, but more and more tension eventually becomes counterproductive and results in exhaustion.

The Human Function Curve explains this very well:

Human Function Curve

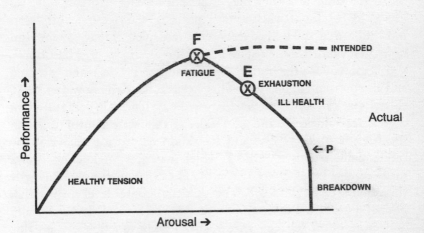

Source: Dr P. G. F. Nixon

In the above diagram the performance curve illustrates that increasing tension, or effort, can also increase your performance – up to a certain point: point F. The F stands for fatigue, and once we have reached this point it is generally useless to continue because our performance, or coping ability, begins to deteriorate. We often imagine we are still functioning well, continuing onwards and upwards towards our goal and maintaining our intended level of perfomance, which is indicated by the broken line. But this is illusory. The real performance actually begins to dip into a downwards slope, illustrating that the more fatigued we are the less capable we are of achieving, or coping; the performance level drops off, and things we could do quite easily when rested, require extra effort when we are tired. Struggling to maintain the intended level of performance hastens the downhill course and if you persist in pushing yourself on, you will eventually reach point E, which stands for exhaustion. Many people hover between point F and point E a lot of the time, and they may experience frequent minor illnesses like colds or flu in this state – nothing serious, but this is an indication that the body's resources are depleted, that you are 'run down'. At point E – in a state of extreme tiredness or exhaustion – you begin to lose the ability to discriminate between the essential and the inessential: between what needs to be done now and those things that can wait – so you are usually trying to do everything, in a 'headless chicken' kind of mode. If this state continues, with insufficient time for rest and relaxation to provide recovery, the individual descends to point P, which indicates the likelihood of a more serious breakdown of health. The bottom line explains why this should be so. You will note that the arousal level for internal bodily systems increases the more fatigued we are. It takes more and more effort to keep an exhausted body functioning and this eventually results in some kind of breakdown of function.

The perfect way to function is to put in as much effort and tension as necessary until you feel tired. At that point – point F – stop for a while and relax, reduce effort, rest, practise deep relaxation or sleep to restore your resources and your ability to cope. Functioning in this way means you always have sufficient energy and never push yourself onto the downslope. Don't get caught in the vicious circle, explained below, and don't rely on cups of coffee or alcohol to keep you going when your body is sending you messages of fatigue!

Caught in a vicious circle

A vicious circle can be set in motion: the more exhausted you are, the fewer resources you have to cope, so life can then begin to seem threatening and overwhelming. You therefore tense up more tightly to fight the perceived threat, becoming more depleted the longer this continues. The more fatigued you are, the more life's demands seem like threats; the more relaxed and refreshed you are the more life's demands will seem like interesting challenges to your creativity and resourcefulness.

It is vital to learn to cut through this vicious circle and switch off the racing mind and unhealthily aroused body. As I said above, unrelieved tension and pressure will sooner or later result in breakdown of either physical or mental health – or both. It may not be dramatic at first, but if you continually push yourself too hard, you will gradually notice that your efficiency level has deteriorated and you cannot achieve as you used to – in fact, everything begins to feel like a strain, as you find it harder and harder to cope. This is a warning signal. When most of the things you face each day feel a strain to deal with, you have reached a dangerous level of fatigue, and must take time off to reassess how you are living your life. You can push yourself occasionally, but not as a way of life. You cannot sprint a marathon, and life is a marathon! Therefore, you need to pace yourself in order to thrive happily right up to the end.

A comedian at the Edinburgh Festival (whose name I do not know – apologies!), echoed this thought with the following ditty:

It's a marathon
It's not a sprint
It's a dance
It's not a race!

I like that! Perhaps copy it out and pin it up where you will see it frequently. You could also copy out the Human Function Curve and put that up in some obvious place, and just keep checking where you feel you are on the curve. It is a very useful barometer for a quick check on the state of your life. Try to stay on the up-curve, but if you do tip over the top, then rest as soon as you can, or practise the deep relaxation routine at the end of this chapter, and bring yourself back into the healthy tension area.

How to release tension at regular intervals

The routines outlined on the following pages will help to reduce the tension level from moment to moment and day to day, by unwinding your muscles and loosening you up. You can release tension by practising these simple movements at regular intervals, stretching out those tightly held muscle groups and allowing them to relax.

This routine is designed to be used at any time and almost anywhere, whenever you recognise that you have tightened up – and it is very enlivening if you have become too static. Try all the movements to begin with, and then pick out the ones that are most useful and work best for you. A good time to use some of them is before you go into an important meeting or event, as they really do relax you and free up your thinking as well.

These loosening movements, calm diaphragmatic breathing and the deep relaxation routine are also on my audio cassette and CD: details of how you can order these can be found at the back of the book.

Loosening and stretching routine

Head and neck movements
- Stretch your neck muscles by turning your head to the right, looking over your right shoulder as if you were trying to see someone standing behind you. Feel the stretch on the opposite side of your neck and hold the position for a few seconds; then turn to the left, looking over your left

shoulder and hold again, feeling the stretch. Keep your body facing forwards. Repeat six times each side, turning your head as far as feels comfortable; don't strain. This is very good for loosening you when you've been sitting at your PC for long periods. I also often do this one a couple of times when sitting in the bus or train, pretending I'm looking out of the window at something behind me. Do make sure you are not clenching your teeth – this applies to all the movements.

- Tip your head over towards your right shoulder, as if you were trying to touch your shoulder with your ear. Keep your head facing forwards. Hold for a few seconds and feel the stretch in the muscles on the opposite side. Now repeat, tipping your head over towards the left shoulder. Again, hold for a moment and feel the stretch in the muscles on the opposite side. Repeat this movement about six times each side, or as many as you have time for. This is a good one to practise when stopped at traffic lights or in a traffic jam.

- Tip your head out and forwards, and feel the stretch in the back of the neck and in the upper part of your back. (This may make you yawn, which is a very good sign, it means the energy is shifting). Now tip your head out and backwards – not too far, as this squashes the upper spine too much. Feel the stretch in your throat and jaw area, and let your jaw hang down loosely. Repeat these movements about six times each, and always finish on a forward one, so that the vertebrae in the back of the neck are nicely stretched. They become compressed, with the weight of the head always pushing down on them, and need frequent stretching and releasing. It is only when the head is supported that the neck muscles can fully relax, so they work very hard all day. When you are sitting at home, try to have your head supported by the back of a chair or by a cushion placed between your head and the wall to give them some rest. A headrest in the car is also releasing for neck muscles.

Shoulders

- Circle your right shoulder backwards six times and then forwards six times.

- Circle your left shoulder backwards six times and then forwards six times.

- Circle both shoulders backwards four times; this should leave them less rounded and not hunched up.

- Shrug your shoulders up and then let them drop. Do this a number of times and register what it actually feels like to drop your shoulders. Drop them many times a day. Then pull them down a little further and feel the muscles stretching. Much tension is carried in our shoulders and neck muscles, which is very wearing.

Practise these shoulder movements frequently through the day wherever you are: at your PC, standing beside the fax machine or photocopier, waiting for the lift or standing in a queue at the supermarket. Instead of fuming at getting held up anywhere, be thankful for an opportunity to unwind and stretch your tightly held muscles.

S – T – R – E – T – C – H

- In fact, stretch at every opportunity! If you have been sitting in a static position, at a keyboard, on the telephone, reading, in a meeting, watching television, etc., then have frequent stretches. Stretch out your arms and your hands, especially your fingers and thumbs. Try stretching your arms out at either side of your body, away from your body, and then stretch your hands backwards almost at right angles to your arms. Feel how good it is to stretch out muscles that have been contracted for long periods.

Legs and feet

- Stretch your legs and feet if you have been sitting for any length of time, at a desk, in a plane or train, at a meeting, or sitting for hours watching TV. Get up if you can and shake your legs the way you see swimmers and athletes loosening up before a race. Jogging on the spot is a another good way to get some movement into your legs in a small space (you can even do it in the loo!), and this also enlivens your whole body – it's a good way to wake yourself up if you've started feeling sleepy. An actress friend of mine jumps up and down a few times just before she goes into an audition: she maintains it puts colour in her cheeks, a sparkle in her eyes and makes her feel alert. I sometimes use this warm-up exercise before an important meeting (you can do it in the lift) or even before I am about to see a client, when I know I am going to have to sit for a while.

- If you cannot stand up, then just move your feet about; this is important to do when you're sitting at a desk all day. Point your toes up towards your knees to stretch your calf muscles, then push your toes down as hard as you can to stretch your shin muscles. (If you suffer from cramp, don't hold this movement too long.) Stretch your entire leg by pushing your heels away from you. Circle your ankles, first in one direction, then the other, to help your circulation. This movement is particularly important for older people who often spend many hours sitting still, and can develop leg ulcers if circulation becomes too sluggish. All these movements are also especially good for you if sitting in a plane for long periods, so as to avoid the problem of deep vein thrombosis. Another that helps in the confined space of a plane is to lift each knee up, by alternately lifting each foot off the floor a few times. All of this applies equally if you are travelling on a long coach journey. Keep moving your feet and legs, at regular intervals, to ensure good blood circulation.

Arms and hands

- If your hands have been held in a tense position for a while, bent over a keyboard, holding the telephone or the steering wheel of your car, or while washing up, writing, painting or playing a musical instrument, then shake them frequently, as if you had just washed them and had no towel, so you have to shake them dry – shake vigorously to dispel the tension. Then stretch the fingers and thumbs out straight and hold for a second or two. This relaxes the hands very effectively and makes them more supple and dexterous. Do it often throughout the day; try to do it between different tasks, and also during certain activities – for example, shake one hand whilst holding the telephone with the other, and then change hands.

- When you're walking along the street shake your hands from time to time just to ensure they are not tightly clenched. Also, wiggle your fingers frequently to relax them.

- To reduce tension in your arms, shake them in a rotating movement, the way a swimmer does when limbering up before a race. Feel the shake – the wobble – going all the way up into your upper arm. This can be done standing or sitting, and is a good movement to do frequently if you're sitting at a computer all day. It's very releasing.

Then stretch your arms out either side of your body, as I described above, and now stretch your wrists so that you push your hands backwards, more or less at right angles to your arms. This is wonderfully releasing, combined with the shaking, if your arms and hands have been held in a fairly static position for some time. Again, this can be practised sitting or standing.

The next set of movements are best done standing up:

- Swing your arms backwards and forwards rhythmically. Swing them up in front of you to shoulder height, then let them drop – just let them go – and experience the feeling of letting your arms drop naturally. Keep swinging them for a few moments – up and drop, up and drop – and enjoy this carefree movement. This is a good exercise to do while waiting for the kettle to boil, or standing by the photocopier. Even talking on the phone, you could swing one arm for a few moments, then change the phone into the other hand and swing the free arm. Just fit all these movements in between and around your everyday activities. This way you transform stressful occurrences – like the incessant telephone – into relaxing exercises.

- Twist your body from side to side from the hips, swinging your shoulders round to the right, then the left, letting your arms swing round as if they were ribbons hanging from your shoulder joints. Let your arms flop and fold round your body at the front and back as they follow the twisting movement. This also feels wonderfully carefree; it is the sort of movement you might see a child doing in the park just for the fun of it. Get back into that child-like sense of being entirely in the present moment, not thinking of what has to be done next, but simply standing and swinging your body and arms. You could even hum a little tune to yourself!

- Stretch your arms full out and then circle them backwards about eight times; feel how this large movement helps you breathe more deeply – how your breath feels released from tight bands constricting your middle.

- Circle your arms forward about eight times: this is very releasing for your upper back muscles, the muscles around your shoulder blades, and is said to prevent Dowager's Hump.

Y – A – W – N

- Yawn as often as possible! It is very good for you. When the body yawns, it is trying to gain more oxygen. The oxygen we take in when we breathe is our most important source of energy. We can do without food for days but we can survive without oxygen for only two minutes; yet so many people hold their breath much of the time, or breathe shallowly in their upper chest, and therefore receive insufficient oxygen to support them in their activities. (There is more on breathing at the end of the chapter; also see page 108.)

- One way to make yourself yawn is to push your chin down towards your chest and breathe in deeply through your nose, keeping your mouth closed. You will feel a lovely deep yawn starting at the bottom of your lungs and gradually rising up your chest, expanding your ribcage outwards, until it reaches your mouth and is expelled. Enjoy yawning, it is not bad manners, it is essential – although perhaps not in front of your mother-in-law!

Smile!

- It is amazing how much better you feel if you put your mouth into a smile – even when you think there is nothing to smile about. It has a psychological effect, but it also affects your face muscles and relaxes them. Just try frowning and see how tight your face feels, then smile and feel the difference. (You use far more muscles for frowning than for smiling.) And an added benefit is that when you relax muscles your blood vessels dilate (widen) increasing blood flow – in this case to your brain. So, when you smile your brain receives more oxygen and nutrients with the increased blood supply, which helps you think more clearly. Experience how a smile puts you back in control!

Breathing

- Whenever you have to perform any action or activity that is a bit of a strain, always breathe out at the moment of greatest effort. Most people breathe in when making a physical effort, but you should use your breath to assist you and this is achieved by breathing out – not in – and not by holding your breath. The exhalation gives you extra strength; you have the force of the breath behind the effort. Don't forget to breathe in first, of course, but do not hold your breath, as this will increase the strain on the body. Calm, diaphragmatic breathing is outlined at the end of the chapter.

- Try not to keep yourself wound up in tense alertness all the time, as it wears you out. Use any annoying situation as an opportunity to remind yourself to unwind. If you are kept waiting by a colleague, friend, your children or your partner, don't get wound up – stretch and let go. Think of it as putting yourself back into neutral – into a resting state, ready for action when needed, but not in tension when not necessary.

Let irritating situations be your triggers to stretch, unwind and let go. Allow the relaxation response to take over from the stress response – and lengthen your life!

Massage

It is wonderful to receive a massage from someone else, either a professional or one's partner, because massage helps to loosen tightly held muscles, and helps them release their waste products more completely. This is mainly lactic acid, and when there is a build up of toxic waste muscles often feel very sore when touched. Once they relax, however, the waste can be carried away by the increased blood flow – another very good reason to release the tension at every possible opportunity.

Aromatherapy is a particularly therapeutic form of massage because of the wonderfully fragrant essential oils that induce a calm and relaxed state of mind, as well as of body – they really do work! Other forms of massage which developed in the East are now available almost everywhere, such as Japanese **shiatsu**, and **Do-In** which is a form of self-massage based on pressure points similar to acupuncture, combined with yoga postures. Another therapeutic, releasing technique is the **Metamorphic Technique**, where the practitioner lightly touches the spinal reflex points on the feet, hands and head, assisting a person's innate intelligence to move them towards whatever is necessary for that individual in terms of their healing or transformation or realisation of their potential.

However, if you cannot persuade your partner, and the bank balance precludes booking up with a professional, you can do a lot to help yourself by massaging your shoulders and neck frequently, and also your leg muscles, feet, hands and head.

- Use your fingertips to massage your shoulders, working outwards from where your neck joins your shoulders in a circular movement. Those muscles at the point where the neck and upper back meet are usually very tense and need a lot of massage and easing out. As they release, you should find yourself yawning again. This is a sign that you are getting more relaxed, and your breath is releasing.

- Massage your neck by tipping your head slightly back to relax the muscles, then take hold of the skin, squeeze and let go, gently working upwards to your head. Then, with the fingers of both hands, massage in circular movements either side of your spine, again working upwards from the base of the neck to the base of your skull. Now massage firmly across the back of the head, and slowly work your way up the back of your head, moving the scalp as you go until you reach the crown. Massage firmly across the top of your scalp as you do when shampooing your hair. Feel the wonderful release as you move your scalp; this will often unlock tensions in the face as well. You can frequently shift a headache by massaging your head and neck.

- Massage your jaw, making circular movements with your fingertips, letting your mouth hang open. Many tension headaches are caused by clenched teeth, and also by continual frowning.

- Massage your forehead by smoothing outwards with your fingertips from the centre towards the temples at each side. Imagine your forehead widening. Then, gently smooth your forehead upwards from your eyebrows to your hairline; feel as if your forehead is getting higher. Imagine all the worry lines are being smoothed away. Tell yourself that your forehead is wide, high, smooth and calm.

- Massage your thigh muscles by squeezing and letting go, and by placing your hands firmly on the tops of the thighs and wobbling the muscles from your groin to your knees. Massage, rub and squeeze around your knees, especially just above the knee where a swelling can sometimes develop. Working around this area helps prevent fluid build-up, which causes the puffiness. Then work on down the leg, squeezing and rubbing the shin muscles in the front and gently squeezing and wobbling the calf muscles on the back of the leg.

- A foot massage can be very soothing and will help you to let go and feel at ease with yourself and the world. Gently rub your toes, one by one, especially working around the joints. Rub the soles of your feet with your thumbs in circular movements. A releasing therapy is **Reflexology**:

this is massage of the feet, concentrating on specific points, said to relate to different organs in the body. They are similar to acupuncture points. It can sometimes be quite painful, but is very effective at clearing energy blocks and helping in the relief of certain problems. It can also unlock suppressed emotion, which can be extremely healing.

- Massage your hands by rubbing them gently together as if you were rubbing in hand cream, and then with one hand gently rub the fingers of the other hand, one at a time; this feels very comforting.

Deep relaxation routine

Now we have come to the secret weapon! When you have mastered deep relaxation you have a powerful antidote to whatever life throws at you. Deep relaxation is an elixir: a sovereign remedy for life's disturbances. It is deeply restorative, releasing stress and distress of mind and emotions, puts you back to a state of harmony and assists healing, repair and replenishment of the body's forces.

You should try to practise the routine outlined below for half an hour every day. You have to do it to experience how wonderful it is. The cumulative effects are very powerful. If you do not have my tape or CD, then I suggest you record this routine onto a blank tape, using a gentle, calm and rhythmical tone of voice, pausing between each instruction. Or ask a friend to record it for you.

- Lie down on a firm surface, a bed or sofa, or on the floor. Place a small cushion under your head and a large cushion or pillow under your thighs to take the strain off your abdomen and ease the small of your back. Make sure that you are warm, as you cannot relax completely if you are cold. It is a good idea to cover yourself with a rug or blanket, as your body temperature falls when you relax deeply, because your heart rate slows down a little and your blood pressure drops. This is why regular practice of deep relaxation is especially good for anyone who suffers from high blood pressure.

- Become aware of your shoulders and pull them down towards your hips (the opposite of shrugging), hold them down for a few seconds and then let them go. Now feel as if your shoulders are tipping back towards the support you are lying on, i.e. the bed, sofa or floor.

- Become aware of your arms. Move your arms a little away from the sides of your body, and bend your elbows slightly outwards. Let your hands rest on your lower abdomen or either side of your body. Now push your arms down into the support, hold for a moment and then stop pushing. Feel your arms getting heavier. Tell yourself to let go more and more through the muscles in your arms. Feel them being completely held by the support. Let go a little more.

- Now be aware of your hands. With your hands still supported, either beside you or resting on your lower abdomen, stretch out your fingers and thumbs. Hold the stretch for a few seconds and then let your fingers flop. Let them go limp, not holding onto anything – not clasped together – and feel your hands completely still and relaxed. There is nothing for them to do right now, just rest. Feel how calming it is to have completely relaxed hands.

- Now be aware of your legs. Push your legs down into the support, hold for a few seconds, then let go. Now point your toes down, stretching your feet away from you, to stretch the muscles in your lower legs. Hold for a second or two (not too long, as this can cause cramp) and then stop and let your feet flop outwards. Now, let your legs fall a little more apart and let your knees roll outwards. Feel your legs sinking down into the support. Let go a little more. Feel your legs becoming heavier and completely relaxed.

- Now be aware of your abdominal muscles below the waist. As you breathe out, let these muscles feel loose, limp and easy – no holding on. Now feel your buttock muscles letting go. Feel the whole of your lower body being held more fully and relaxing more completely.

- Now be aware of your diaphragm, just above your waist. Feel as if this part of you is expanding slightly. Just let go all around your middle, and feel your easy breathing in this area. Feel your ribcage moving outwards as you breathe in, and feel your diaphragm expanding. As you breathe out slowly, feel yourself relaxing – feel your body letting go more deeply. It is always the out-breath that relaxes you. Take a few moments to experience your calm, rhythmical breathing in your diaphragm – in the middle of your body – breathing out a little more slowly than you breathe in, and feeling yourself letting go more and more deeply.

- Now be aware of your back being supported. Press down a little more heavily into the support, hold for a few seconds, then stop pushing and let go. Feel your whole body being held a little more completely than before. Now let go even more deeply.

- Now be aware of your mouth and jaw. Make sure your top and bottom teeth are slightly apart, not clenched together. Let your tongue rest near the bottom of your mouth, behind your lower teeth: this is the relaxed position for the tongue. Let your lips touch lightly. Become aware of how it feels to have a relaxed mouth and jaw.

- Now imagine a smile beginning in your mouth and slowly

spreading into your cheeks – feel as if your cheeks are widening out a little.

- Now be aware of your eyes. Close your eyelids lightly, let your eye muscles relax – there is nothing to focus on, or stare at. Let your eye muscles rest, and enjoy the peace that comes from shutting out all visual stimuli for a while.

- Now be aware of your forehead. Imagine gentle fingers smoothing your forehead outwards from the centre to the temples at either side. Feel as if your forehead is widening out. Imagine all the worry lines are being smoothed away. Now imagine your forehead is being gently smoothed upwards from your eyebrows to your hairline. Feel as if your forehead is becoming higher. Feel a sense of having a high, wide brow that is serene and smooth.

- Now imagine gentle hands are massaging over your scalp: up over the top of your head and down the back of your head. Feel as if your whole head area is expanding a little. Let go through all the muscles in your scalp. Relax your scalp and head.

- Now just enjoy the feeling of being relaxed. Enjoy the feeling of ease. Rest in the calm and peace that come with letting go deeply and completely.

- Stay in this relaxed feeling, and rest your mind by picturing a beautiful, peaceful place: somewhere you would like to be right now. Rest in this beautiful place in your imagination for a few minutes. Enjoy being there and taking a little time away from the outside world. Be aware that this is a very healthy thing to do. You are not wasting your time – you are using time very creatively to restore your energy and vitality.

- Hold the awareness that all the repair processes of the body are enhanced and the immune system is boosted, when you are in this state of deep relaxation.

- When you wish to come back into normal alertness, do so gently and slowly. First, gently wiggle your fingers and toes; then have a gentle stretch – stretch out your arms, hands, fingers, then your legs, feet and toes. Push your heels away from you to stretch out your spine and body. Roll onto your side for a moment or two, and finally, when you are ready, sit up slowly. Always return slowly from deep relaxation, as all the systems in the body have slowed down and you do not want to shock or strain them. Just sit still for a few moments, taking plenty of time to return to your normal, everyday awareness. Then stand up slowly, so as not to feel dizzy; try to move and speak a little more slowly than you usually do for as long as you can. Just keep that feeling of calm with you for as long as possible. Half an hour is an ideal time span for this deep, restorative relaxation, but if you want to drift off to sleep for a short while afterwards that is fine. In fact, you will find that even just ten or fifteen minutes sleep after completing the full relaxation will be extraordinarily refreshing. This routine is a wonderful way to send yourself to sleep at night but do try to practise it at other times, to experience its unique benefits, and not merely as a prelude to your night's sleep.

Practising this deep relaxation routine frequently will build more calm into you at all levels; so do persevere with it even if, at first, it is not easy to be still. You have to just let it happen – don't try too hard – and eventually you will begin to experience the cumulative effect, and you will be able to switch into a calm state with ease. Take regular time out to experience this altered state and see it as a way to pay in to your energy account, to build reserves.

Calm breathing

This exercise will restore you to feeling calm and at ease when you don't have time, or it's not appropriate, to practise the deep relaxation technique, and it can be used to dispel difficult or negative emotions. Whenever you have become wound up, anxious, fearful, angry or stressed generally, you will find this technique is a great help in putting you back in control and restoring your equilibrium. This is the way your body is designed to breathe for normal, everyday activities. Practice this routine, and become familiar with how correct breathing feels and where in your body you should feel the rise and fall of your breath. This way, you will become skilled at controlling your breathing for when you actually need to. As I have explained on page 108, in the stress response our breathing is altered (you may like to re-read the description to remind yourself) and the routine outlined below is the way to return to normal functioning: i.e. to breathing as nature intended, and to feeling peaceful.

This routine can be practised sitting or lying down; if you are sitting, sit well back in your chair, letting the back of the chair support your spine, with your legs uncrossed and both feet on the ground.

- First, breathe out; let your breath out in a slow sigh. Now breathe in slowly, feeling your diaphragm (just above your waist) expand outwards. As you breathe out again, say to yourself, 'Let go,' and feel yourself beginning to release the tensions in your body.

- Now breathe in again, feeling your ribcage on either side of your body expand sideways, and now slowly exhale, letting your out-breath be a little longer and a little slower than your in-breath.

- Repeat by inhaling slowly. Experience your ribcage spreading sideways and your diaphragm expanding in front of your body. Never hold your breath once you have inhaled, just let your breath out again in a slow sigh. Pause for a second before you breathe in again, as above, feeling the expansion in the middle of your body.

- Continue this rhythm for about five minutes. Concentrate on making sure that you are breathing into the middle of your body, feel that part of you expanding sideways, and let your out-breath always be a little longer and a little slower than your in-breath.

- Practise at first by counting to three as you breathe in, and to four as you breathe out. Do this by saying slowly to yourself as you inhale, 'In, two, three.' Then, as you exhale, say, 'Out, two, three, four.' Continue for about five minutes. This counting is simply to give you the experience of breathing out for a little longer than you breathe in; if it feels wrong, forget the counting and just focus on slightly lengthening your out-breath. Continue to practise for a further five minutes, so that you get into the rhythm, and understand how it should feel.

- Practise this exercise every day, a number of times a day, for just a minute or two, so that when you actually need it, you will be skilled at calming your breathing and bringing it down to your diaphragm, where breathing is designed to take place for ordinary, everyday activities.

- Use this technique to re-establish equilibrium after, or even during, any stressful event; or after a difficult or emotional encounter with someone.

- When you have mastered your breathing, try to imagine that you are breathing out any negative emotions that you are feeling.

- Visualise them floating away on your out-breath, and then breathe in positive emotions, to calm your inner state. For example, breathe in calmness, peace and serenity.

- Also breathe out attitudes that are no longer relevant or useful to you; breathe in an attitude that would be more helpful. For example, breathe in an attitude of tolerance, patience, stability or centredness.

There is an ancient Yoga saying:

'When you can control your breath, you will control your life.'

8

Food to empower you

Food is the fuel on which we run. If you had a beautiful, high-performance car, you would not fuel it on low-grade petrol, and expect it to perform at the height of its power. You would know full well that it could not perform as it was designed to without the best fuel available. How much more is this true of our bodies? The human body is the most amazing and wonderful design imaginable – I don't like calling the body a machine, for it seems somehow reductive, but for this purpose it is worth making the comparison. This incredible vehicle, in which we travel from birth to the grave, can surely not be expected to function at its optimum peak without the best fuel, any more than a car – or, for that matter, a pedigree dog or a thoroughbred race horse. Does it not seem strange that we recognise the fuel needs of our cars more than the fuel needs of ourselves? Or, indeed, that we often feed our prize animals more carefully than we feed ourselves!

Strange as it is, it happens to be true. Of course, the reason for this is that fuelling ourselves is a great deal more complicated than choosing which grade of petrol for our car; the same applies to animal feed. But the point I am trying to make is that we don't give enough thought to what we put into our bodies and we don't really consider it necessary to take the matter seriously. Whereas we know that the results of using the wrong petrol would quickly become apparent, we tend to forget that the results of using the wrong food will also become apparent – albeit in a longer timescale.

Because it can seem too complicated to address this matter of good diet, I want to try to simplify the subject and give you a few tips for maintaining your body at the peak of its powers. For while it is important to support yourself with good nutrition at all times, it is particularly important when you are stressed, strained or overloaded. Equally, it is possible to release stress by using nutrition to power you – think Popeye and spinach!

At times of stress there is often an urge to turn to food and drink which comforts, but this is generally not of the highest quality. Comfort food tends to be high in sugar content and/or fatty in nature: i.e. crisps, chips, fry-ups, ice-cream, sweets, chocolate bars, cakes and biscuits. Low-quality food of this type creates a huge problem for the body, because it provides insufficient quantities of the raw materials necessary for maintaining, and rebuilding, its organs and systems, therefore it adds to the strain. It also causes a lot of toxic waste, making us feel run-down and low in energy, and so we're tempted to reach for another 'treat' to lift us up, in the form of the above mentioned 'foods' plus sweet drinks, caffeine and alcohol. These may give us a quick 'high', but it is not long lasting; it is always followed by the rebound sinking feeling that takes us down. We then reach for more sugar to lift us up again; the vicious circle going round and round. Comfort foods will not harm us too much, if we only indulge in them occasionally, but they do not provide the body with what it needs to produce abundant health and vitality from day to day, or to withstand stress.

It is important to understand that if your body cannot utilise the content of your food to replenish its cells and systems, it has to find something to do with the 'stuff' it has been fed. It has two options: to store it, or to eliminate it. Unfortunately, a great deal of this rubbish is stored and it fatigues you. Just as each of us becomes stressed when overwhelmed with too much to do, so the organs in the body can become equally overwhelmed when we present them with too much work in the form of substances they cannot absorb or use; this stresses them and, over time, can cause them to cease to function adequately, or to break down completely.

For a power burst we need fresh, living food rich in vitamins, minerals and other nutrients, bursting with vitality, in contrast to the dead, packaged and processed offerings that proliferate on our supermarket shelves.

One quick pointer for how to eat healthily is to imagine a huge plate, and picture it containing everything you might eat in the course of a day. You would have a good, healthy diet if one half of that plate contained vegetables (preferably both raw and cooked) salad stuffs, fresh fruit, nuts and seeds. The remaining half would be divided more or less equally between protein and complex carbohydrates such as bread, grains (including cereals) pasta and pulses, together with a small amount of fats. This could be achieved by ensuring that one meal per day – preferably at lunch time – consisted of a huge salad, containing as many uncooked vegetables as possible, as well as all the obvious salad ingredients, accompanied by perhaps a jacket potato and a small amount of protein. You could also include some cooked vegetables as well; with this combination you would be giving yourself a plentiful supply of vital energy to cope with the rest of the day. Later on, in the early evening, you could indulge yourself with the heavier foods, such as pasta, sauces, breads, cheeses, as well as cakes or puddings – if you must!

The heavier foods take more energy to digest, and if consumed at breakfast, or in the middle of the day, they will make you feel very tired due to using up the energy you need for your day's productivity. It is interesting to note that digesting a large, three-course meal uses more energy than almost any activity you might engage in. For this reason, I do not agree with the pundits who maintain you must eat a hearty breakfast. The best things to eat for breakfast are fruit, yogurt or a whole grain cereal with skimmed milk and little, or no, sugar; huge fry-ups simply produce much toxic waste and make you feel sleepy!

Of course, food is more than just fuel, it also plays an essential part in maintaining good health and preventing disease. Thus, another quick pointer I should like to give you is this: one of the most important things to do for your body is to protect it from free radicals. Free radicals are harmful oxygen molecules that naturally accumulate in the body and damage healthy tissues, causing changes in cells that can lead to cancer, heart disease and other serious conditions, as well as being responsible for ageing. What is needed to counteract these predators are antioxidants, which are protective compounds that either stop the formation of free radicals, or disable them before they do harm. Research suggests that the more antioxidants we get in our diets, the less likely we are to die of cancer. The most studied and most powerful antioxidants are vitamins C and E, and beta-carotene which is contained in many fruits and vegetables ranging from yellow to rich orange to red hues, such as carrots, red peppers, apricots and cantaloupe melons (especially rich in both beta-carotene and vitamin C), as well as carotenoids found in dark green, leafy vegetables like broccoli, cabbage, watercress and spinach. Antioxidant properties are also found in green and black teas. I shall mention more on this later.

Below are some essential guidelines for eating for health and powerful energy.

Eat less

Sugar

In the stress response, your body releases extra sugar (see page 102), so it needs less by mouth. Sugar provides empty calories; it gives you energy for physical exertion, but no essential raw materials for replenishing the cells of the body. You may get an immediate 'high' from sugary foods or drinks, but this wears off very quickly and is followed by a sudden drop in energy and a 'low feeling', so while your taste buds may enjoy sugar, overindulging can cause depressed moods. Also, if you do not use up the energy, those extra calories will simply cause overweight. High sugar intake puts a strain on the pancreas for extra insulin, which can lead to malfunction. By reducing sugar you also reduce the risk of coronary heart disease. Check labels for hidden sugar in foods such as cereals, tinned fruit and vegetables, bread, sauces, etc. Eat natural sugar found in fresh and dried fruit, raisins, dates, black strap molasses and pure honey, or buy pure fructose (fruit sugar) from health food stores.

Fat

Fat should not be cut out altogether: it is necessary for the absorption of the fat-soluble vitamins A, D, E and K, for maintaining healthy cell membranes and for building a strong immune system. It is only harmful when eaten to excess, and should make up no more than 30 per cent of your daily calorie intake, of which only 10 per cent should be saturated fat (animal fat). Use olive oil instead of butter or lard, especially for cooking, as it does not oxidise when heated, which other vegetable oils do, producing harmful free radicals. Olive oil is a monounsaturated fat and has beneficial properties for health, as proven in Mediterranean countries where consumption is high, but heart disease is surprisingly low. However, it is very fattening, so consume in moderation; fats contain approximately twice as many calories as carbohydrates and proteins. All oils should be refrigerated to prevent them from turning rancid, another cause of free radicals. Saturated fats found in red meat and dairy produce are particularly harmful when you are in the stress response, due to the body's production of extra cholesterol and free fatty acids to aid you in 'Fight or Flight'. Grill or bake foods rather than frying in fat, and remember the 'hidden' fats in food like pork, breast of lamb, sausages, bacon, egg yolks, gravy, cheese, puddings, biscuits and pastries – and chocolate!

Salt

The average person needs approximately one-third of a teaspoon of salt (sodium chloride) per day. Strenuous exercise and excessive sweating in hot weather could increase your salt needs due to high amounts being lost in your sweat, but most people consume far more salt than necessary for the body's healthy function. Excessive sodium can damage your kidneys and cause high blood pressure, strokes and heart failure. Fluid retention due to potassium loss can also result from a diet high in salt, contributing to premenstrual tension and causing serious problems during pregnancy. Avoid too many salty snacks, like salted nuts and crisps, and savoury or cheese biscuits. Hard cheeses have a high salt content, as do tinned and processed foods, especially processed meats. Try not to add extra salt to food on your plate and use small amounts when cooking: enhance flavours with herbs, lemon juice or spices. If a low-salt diet is unpalatable for you, try using potassium chloride, which is stocked at most health food stores instead of sodium chloride. Best of all is to train your taste buds not to need too much salt.

Eat more

Fresh vegetables
Fresh vegetables are one of the best ways to combat those harmful free radicals for they are bursting with antioxidant vitamins and many other important nutrients. Preferably eat vegetables raw – most vegetables taste delicious in their uncooked state. When cooking, steam or use very little water to avoid losing too many vitamins, or use the vegetable water for soups, sauces, stews or simply as a drink. If fresh vegetables are not available, the best alternative is frozen, as their vitality is preserved up to a point by the freezing process. You can see the abundant life in fresh vegetables which, of course, is transmitted into your system when you eat them; if you leave them too long you can observe the life-force literally draining away, as they shrivel up. Whenever possible, choose organically grown produce to avoid the toxins of chemical pesticides and fertilizers, which overload the body with chemical waste and require valuable energy to eliminate. You should try to eat three to five portions of vegetables, both raw and cooked, each day.

Salad foods

All the foods normally associated with salad, such as lettuce, cucumber, tomatoes, mushrooms, peppers, celery, celeriac (celery root), radishes, avocados, endive, fennel, watercress, parsley, etc. are also brimming with vitamins and minerals, which give you vitality and energy. As cooking destroys many of these nutrients it is important to obtain maximum nutritional value by eating salad foods regularly. The only reservation here is in the consumption of raw mushrooms, which have been found to contain a compound which could be poisonous in large amounts. Cooking destroys this culprit so, just to be safe, keep raw mushrooms to a minimum. Another important factor is that these foodstuffs have a high water content, which assists in their assimilation and aids your digestion and your elimination processes. It is more difficult for the body to digest and absorb concentrated foods such as protein and carbohydrate, which should be eaten in smaller amounts.

Fresh fruit

This is another vital, high water-content food (80–90 per cent water content), which helps to cleanse the body of toxic waste. Fruit should always be eaten uncooked as cooking turns it acidic, forcing the body to use precious energy to neutralize it; cooking also destroys most, if not all, of its health-giving nutrients. Fruit is considered to be the most beneficial food of all, supplying every nutrient needed for optimum health: glucose, amino acids, fatty acids, minerals and vitamins. It requires minimum energy for its digestion, absorption and assimilation. Fruit should be eaten on an empty stomach, as it is digested very quickly, only remaining in the stomach for about 30 minutes before passing into the intestines. If you eat fruit at the end of a meal, it gets held up in the stomach behind the other food and begins to ferment, losing its goodness and often causing flatulence and discomfort. So eat it first thing in the morning: it will supply you with plenty of energy to face the day and assist in the body's elimination processes. Try to eat at least one piece of fruit per day, more if possible. When you crave a snack between meals eat fruit or raw vegetables, or nuts and seeds (seeds are very potent energy providers, as they are full of vitality, or life-forces; nuts are fattening, so go easy on them).

Fibre

Fibre is one of the most essential components of a healthy diet, especially when you are stressed. Fibre assists the efficient elimination of toxins and waste, one of the main keys to maintaining good health. It is difficult for the body to remain healthy if poisons are circulating and toxic waste material is being stored rather than excreted. Fibre acts like a sponge or blotting paper in the body by absorbing undigested food, toxins and excess cholesterol – including the cholesterol produced internally as a response to stress – and ushers them out of the body. Foods containing fibre, or roughage, are: fresh fruit, vegetables (especially raw vegetables), whole grains like brown rice, oats (particularly good at soaking up cholesterol), wheatgerm, millet, rye, barley, maize, muesli (check for added sugar), wholewheat pasta, wholemeal bread and crispbreads, high-fibre biscuits, oatcakes, high-fibre cereals like All Bran, baked potatoes, baked beans, seeds, sweetcorn, unsalted nuts and pulses like lentils, peas, mung beans, kidney beans and aduki beans. Sufficient fibre will be obtained from a mixed diet of the above foods.

Good and Poor Choices in a Stress-releasing Diet

BREAKFAST

Good choices	Poor choices
✓ Banana and/or yoghurt, fresh mixed-fruit salad	X No breakfast (especially children)
✓ Grapefruit, melon	X Tinned fruit in sugary syrup
✓ Muesli or high-fibre cereal, with skimmed milk, unrefined sugar or fructose (fruit sugar)	X Low-fibre, sugar-enriched cereal
✓ Wholewheat toast or crispbread with honey, sugar-free jam, or low-salt, savoury spread	X Fried foods such as egg, bacon, sausages, fried bread, etc.
	X White, refined-flour bread with high-sugar jam/syrup

✓ Boiled/scrambled egg (no more than 3 or 4 times a week)

✓ Fruit juice, tea, herb tea, decaffeinated coffee or dandelion coffee

X Sugary biscuits

X Strong coffee with lots of sugar

X Sweets, chocolate bars, crisps

LUNCH

Good choices

✓ Melon, fresh fruit cocktail

✓ Huge salad with as many raw vegetables as possible and/or cooked fresh vegetables

✓ Jacket potato (eat skin)

✓ Rice (preferably brown)

✓ Small amount of protein (meat 2–4 times per week; fish 2–3 times per week)

✓ Cauliflower cheese

✓ Small vegetable pasta dish

✓ Soup, wholemeal bread, salad

✓ Baked beans, scrambled egg

✓ Omelette, vegeburger

✓ Mineral water, fruit juice

✓ 1 glass wine, ½ pint beer

Poor choices

X Fried potatoes (have occasionally as a treat)

X Fried fish/sausages/hamburgers (grill them instead)

X No salad or fresh vegetables

X Tinned vegetables (too often)

X Rich, creamy sauces (hard to digest; will make you sleepy)

X Huge pasta dish (have a small portion with salad and/or vegetables)

X Rich, creamy desert

X Sausage, egg and chips

X Sugary soft drinks

X More than 1 unit of alcohol

DINNER

Good choices

✓ Melon, avocado, grapefruit

✓ Prawn or seafood cocktail

✓ Soup (homemade, if possible)

✓ Grilled/roast meat

✓ Baked/grilled fish

✓ Casserole of meat or fish or vegetables

✓ Vegetables au gratin

✓ Pulses, rice

Poor choices

X Processed/high-salt meats

X Smoked fish/meat too often

X Fatty meats – pork, lamb, chicken skin, fatty mince, hamburgers, sausages – more than once per week

X High-cholesterol-forming dishes, sauces with high butter/cream content

✓ Lots of fresh vegetables
✓ Pasta or curry (meat/vegetable)
✓ Low-fat yoghurt/ice cream
✓ Herb/camomile tea

X High sugar/cream content desserts like: ice cream, sorbets, trifles, gateaux, etc.
X Tinned fruit
X Sugary soft drinks
X Strong coffee and/or large quantities of alcohol

Alcohol: consume in moderation with at least 1 or 2 alcohol-free days per week

The 'Poor choices' foods can be consumed occasionally without weakening your health and power too seriously, but they should not form the largest part of your diet. Try to choose most of your foods from the 'Good choices' selection, and you will boost your defences against stress and empower your performance in life.

Eat minimally for maximum alertness

When you particularly wish to be at full throttle it is best to eat minimally. Remembering that large quantities of food require large amounts of energy to digest, it is sensible to free up your energy for a spectacular performance by ingesting small meals. If you have an important meeting during a meal-time, eat some long-lasting energy food about half an hour beforehand – like a banana – to ensure your blood sugar level does not drop too low, and then during the encounter just nibble. Thus you keep your adrenalin flowing and your attention alert. You can eat again after the meeting, if you're starving! But don't fall into the trap of over-indulging on either food or alcohol, and end up finding it hard to keep awake. In fact, studies have shown that those people who always eat fairly small amounts as a way of life tend to be very long lived. Little and often seems to be a better formula than huge meals with long gaps between.

Vitamin and mineral supplements

If you are eating a properly balanced diet, as outlined above, your body should be well buffered against the demands of everyday stresses. However, if your stress levels increase due to excessive sleep loss, chronic fatigue, illness, emotional upset, overcrowding, lack of control, noise pollution or too much change, the extra demands on your adaptive capacities cause every nutrient to be needed in larger-than-usual amounts. Therefore, at those times when the demands on you are extreme, you should take a daily multivitamin and mineral supplement, as well as extra vitamin C (up to 1000 mg per day). The need for vitamin C is increased tremendously by stress, as is the need for pantothenic acid, which can be taken in a tablet form or by eating lots of green leafy vegetables, eggs, wheat bran and peanuts (preferably unsalted). Smoking (a terrible stress for the body, for it is an external source of free radicals as well as toxic chemicals) also increases your vitamin C requirement: in fact, it takes 20 milligrams of vitamin C to neutralise the effect of just one cigarette. Zinc tends to be depleted at times of stress, although beware of taking excess zinc, as this can cause copper deficiency and lead to anaemia. Zinc is found in eggs, meat and seafood (especially oysters). Zinc depletion, however, can lead to reduction of sex hormones, which is why oysters have long been considered an aphrodisiac. If you are under a lot of emotional or mental stress, I would suggest a supplement of the B-complex vitamins, but do not exceed the recommended daily allowance. Supplements should be seen as just that, to be taken alongside a healthy diet, not as substitutes for good food. Never take vitamin pills on an empty stomach, they are too concentrated and need to be mixed with food.

Drink plenty of water

It is desirable to drink about eight glasses, or at least 1.5 litres of water each day. Make sure that you drink at least half a pint of water before retiring to bed, and another half-pint on rising in the morning. Have some bottled water in your bedroom so that you can also drink some if you should wake in the middle of the night. Getting enough water, doctors say, will ensure you never get kidney stones. If you don't drink enough water the body's wastes become concentrated, forming crystals that can bond together and create kidney stones. One way to tell if you are drinking enough water is to observe your urine. Except in the morning, when you haven't had fluids all night, it should be very pale yellow or even clear. If the colour is dark, you should be drinking more water. If you use your car a lot, keep a bottle of mineral water in it, so that you can take frequent drinks. When flying it is particularly important to drink plenty of water, as the air pressure inside the plane dehydrates you. You will feel less jet-lag at the end of your journey if you drink approximately a pint of water per flying hour (although be sensible, if you are flying on very long-haul flights that amount may be excessive). But try not to consume alcohol or coffee, as both dehydrate the body and add to the problem of pressurised cabins.

Drinking plenty of water is extremely important in many ways. It ensures frequent urine excretion and dilutes toxins in the bladder reducing the possibility of bladder infection. Another positive by-product will be a clearer and more youthful skin condition, as the skin becomes more wrinkled when we don't consume enough water.

Alleviating panic attacks and PMS

If we go without food for many hours our blood sugar drops, and this is thought to contribute to panic attacks. When the blood sugar drops below a certain level, the body releases adrenalin to keep us going, and it is this excess of adrenalin that can cause shakiness and the symptoms, and feelings, of panic attacks. So, if you suffer from panic attacks, never go for long periods without eating; make sure that you eat something, preferably of a starchy nature, every three to four hours to keep your blood sugar steady. Look at what I have said about disordered breathing on page 108, as this will also give you more explanations about the causes of, and ways to control, panic attacks.

Eating something at frequent intervals, generally from the carbohydrate foods like bread, pasta, rice or even a few biscuits, also helps with premenstrual syndrome, reducing the symptoms of weepiness, aggression and general mood swings by keeping blood sugar stable. It may also help if you avoid salt, or salty foods, when menstruation is due, as sodium causes fluid retention in body tissues – already a problem at this time of the month – and the resultant bloatedness can give rise to feelings of intense sensitivity, exacerbating irritability and moodiness.

One final power boost

It is said that our bodies were not designed to digest proteins and carbohydrates at the same time, and that eating these two foods in the same meal causes much energy loss, and eventually increased susceptibility to ill-health. This is the thinking behind what is known as the Hay Diet, or Food Combining. You may have heard of these healthful ways of eating, and may wish to try them. Briefly, the theory of the system is that protein foods – meat, fish, poultry, eggs, cheese etc. – and acid fruits should not be eaten at the same meal with starches – bread, potatoes, cereals, grains etc. – and sugary foods. Proteins require acid for their digestion, and carbohydrates require an alkaline milieu in which to be assimilated. When we eat both in the same meal the body produces both acid and alkali in our stomachs, but they tend to neutralise each other, with the result that our foods are not properly digested. It is beyond the scope of this book to expound this theory and system of eating in greater detail, but I recommend two excellent books on the subject, *Fit For Life* by Harvey and Marilyn Diamond (Bantam Books) and *Food Combining For Life* by Doris Grant (Thorsons). You might like to try this way of eating and see for yourself if it boosts your energy and health. I can only say that when I have managed to stick to it, it certainly seems to make me feel more alive and vital, and many friends report the same. It also seems to produce a rather welcome side-effect of weight loss without trying! So I would urge you to explore this food combining philosophy more closely.

So what needs changing?

All this talk of what is the best way to eat may leave you a little bewildered about where, if anywhere, to start to change your eating habits. The best way to begin to address this subject is to work out exactly what you are already eating. I would suggest that you write down everything you have eaten and drunk at the end of each day for a fortnight – or even a month if you can keep it up. You may not like what you see, but you will have your eating habits in front of you, and once you have realised just what you are actually eating, it should not be too difficult to work out where adjustments need to be made – what you need more of and what you need to cut down on – following the guidelines in this chapter. Buy a little notebook to carry around with you, and just jot down everything you eat, as you eat it – include drinks as well.

Try not to eat when you are feeling very stressed and wound up, emotionally upset or angry, because you will not be able to digest your food properly. Remember that in the stress response, the digestive system partially or completely shuts down (see page 106), and so eating in this condition may cause you indigestion, and will certainly mean that you do not receive the full goodness from your food.

Before eating, try to have a few moments of stillness, to calm down and relax; create a beautiful, peaceful environment around you as often as you can, perhaps with candles and soothing music playing. Enjoy your food, love your body, and eat for power and health.

9

It's not what you do,
it's the way that you do it

It is often not so much *what* someone does, but *how* they do it that makes all the difference to their performance in life. One aspect of the *how* is to find your own rhythm and stay in tune with yourself.

Rhythm is an integral part of all life, and the basis of the inner functioning of our bodily systems. When we feel stressed or distressed it is often because we have lost the right kind of rhythm in our lives, or got out of sync with ourselves. Our minds and bodies function better when they have a routine or rhythm. Thus it is important that we find our own personal rhythm for the various aspects of our lives. We need to learn to be in step with ourselves.

We are each unique and have a unique chemical make-up, which fluctuates differently from other people's, so that what works for somebody else doesn't necessarily work for all. Somehow we have to fit our lifestyle to our rhythmic needs, and not the other way round.

Your inner clock

The way to begin with this exercise is to chart your own personal inner clock: your best time of day for different tasks. You may have a rhythm imposed from outside in the sense that you have to adhere to a timetable of work and leisure created by someone else. However, you can still choose the kind of tasks you tackle at different times of the day. For example, I am an owl and not a lark, and I am at my best later in the day, rather than early in the morning. I can tackle mechanical, physical tasks in the morning better than intellectual ones. My thinking becomes clearer and more creative as the day wears on; my most productive time is in the evening, or often in the hours after midnight. I have managed to organise my work life to suit my personal rhythms. I usually tackle mundane administration work in the morning, and exercise my body by walking to the bank, shops, post office and so on. I see a few clients in the afternoon, but the major part of my one-to-one therapy work takes place with people in the evening. As they finish their working day, I am starting that part of mine. I mostly write in the late evening and into the early hours of the morning. If I get onto a particularly good roll of inspiration I may stay up all night writing. But, of course, I can sleep in late next morning, in the same way as performers such as actors and musicians need to do. This suits me. I like a late rhythm – late up, late to bed. If I am forced by outside circumstances into a different rhythm for too long I don't feel peaceful inside. I feel at odds with myself, like I'm crammed into a straightjacket. I can function adequately for a while if I have to work office hours due to running workshops or giving lectures in companies and organisations, but I make sure I get myself back to my natural rhythm as soon as possible.

Well, that's me. What about you? If you are also an owl, then try to organise your work in a similar manner, at least put all the more automatic tasks into the early part of the day, and the more creative work into the second half. Knowing when is your best time means you work with yourself, not against yourself. For instance, if you have to attend an important meeting and you function best later in the day, then make sure you come up with some very good reasons why you cannot have that meeting in the morning! Don't allow yourself to be talked into accommodating someone else's rhythm if you can possibly help it.

If you are a lark then you will be at your brightest first thing in the morning and should ensure that the most important work can be tackled then, as well as organising your most important meetings earlier rather than later in the day. Obviously a problem will arise if your boss is one and you are the other – and similarly with your emotional partner. Then it is going to be a question of the most determined winning! But seriously, if you can recognise this problem for what it is: different personal rhythms, then you may be able to discuss it with the other person and agree a compromise. As well as alternating whose rhythm takes priority, you can also ask for some leniency if you are not at your very best when they are – and think you should be!

Rhythm of different tasks

Try to ensure a rhythm between different types of tasks, and especially between ones that are sedentary and those that involve some moving about. If most of your day is spent sitting – at a computer, drawing board or easel, check-out counter, desk or musical instrument, or whatever – make sure you take regular breaks when you can stretch and move your body. If you work at home, or in a private office, that shouldn't be a problem, so long as you can motivate yourself. If you work in an open-plan office, then make a pretext for walking up to the next floor (don't take the lift!) and do some stretching exercises on the way. At the very least get up and go to the cloakroom if that is the only movement allowed you and do some arm swinging while you are there (see Chapter 7) or some jumping up and down on the spot. Use every opportunity you can for moving around; even run up those stairs, pretending you are in a hurry, or walk up two at a time, to stretch your leg muscles.

Try to ensure you go out at lunchtime as often as possible, so as to exercise a little more, and to breathe in some fresh air. Increased movement will, of course, also make you breathe more deeply and efficiently, for breathing is another very important rhythm that can become erratic and dysfunctional, with unpleasant effects (See Chapter 7 for more on breathing). If you can't move much during your day, try at least to stretch your arms, hands and fingers at frequent intervals: a good way to do this is to hold your arms out at either side of your body – at right angles to your body – and then push your hands back as far as you can by bending at the wrist, so that your hands are now almost at right angles to your arms. This is a good neural stretch, and very releasing. Also shake your hands at regular intervals to shake out the tension. This will keep your hands supple and dextrous. In addition, turn your head from side to side to release your neck, and drop your head sideways towards each shoulder a few times, keeping your face forwards. (This is described more fully in Chapter 7.)

Weekly rhythms

As well as having individual daily rhythms, we have our own personal weekly rhythms. Some people (although probably not many!) are at their best on Mondays and deteriorate as the week moves along. In research studies it has been found that most people are not fully functioning at the height of their powers on Monday, but peak on Tuesdays and Wednesdays, and then begin to lose energy on Thursday, coming back up on Friday with the prospect of the weekend ahead. But, once again, you are a unique individual and need to work out your own best days of the week rather than assume you fall into research categories. The important point is to take advantage of high energy to achieve and create, and to accept that you may have to coast a little when your energy is low. Don't beat yourself up if you have 'off' days. Don't expect to achieve the same amount of output all the time like a machine. You are not a machine; you are a work of art, a creative miracle.

I always try to organise my most important meetings, activities or creative endeavours towards the end of the week, for, just as I function best at the end of the day, I am also at my highest energy levels at the end of the week. Work out, by observing your energy levels, which times in the week you have a peak and when you go into a trough. Mark in your diary when your energy is strong, and when you feel quieter or more passive, over a period of a few months. Then try to organise your work and important schedules around these fluctuations of energy, in a way that supports you and gives you permission to operate in a manner that uses your power when it is most switched on.

Understanding and taking seriously the different rhythms we each work to, can save you and others a lot of stress. I think the most important point is not to feel guilty because your best time may differ from someone else's. You are you. You are unique, and nowhere is it written that you should not be who you are but should be someone else. It is extremely important to remember this and remind yourself of it frequently.

So much of our internal stress comes from not accepting ourselves, criticising ourselves, or colluding with others' criticisms.

The monthly cycle

This particular rhythm is the one that has received most attention, and the study of bio-rhythms is based on this. These rhythms are the fluctuations of energies throughout the lunar cycle and I would suggest that you browse in your local bookstore for books specialising in this subject, as it is beyond the scope of this book to elaborate fully here. Each person's reactions to the waxing and waning moon will be unique up to a point, although, of course, we are all subject to outside cosmic energies, electrical vibrations and the chemical composition of our immediate environment. However, one aspect that could be important for you, is to note that universal energy is said to be greater during the first half of the moon's cycle; that is, from the new moon period to the full moon. This is the time to be active, energetic and outward looking. At the midpoint, as the full moon begins to wane, the cosmic energies change and gradually dwindle. So that during the second half of the cycle you may feel less expansive, quieter and more introspective. How profoundly this affects you will depend on your unique make-up and, to a certain extent, on where in the yearly cycle you were born. For example, the water signs like Pisces, Cancer and Scorpio will be more affected by the moon cycle than the Earth signs. At the changeover time you should take extra care, as this is a vulnerable time when accidents tend to happen (around the full moon). Of course, women's monthly menstruation cycles will affect their energy levels, and you may find that there is a correlation with the lunar cycle.

Rhythmical movements

Another aspect of rhythm is how we move. Do you move rhythmically or jerkily? Because the basis of our bodily systems is a continual state of rhythm, we feel best when we move rhythmically. It is much less tiring to perform any action rhythmically, in a flowing movement, rather than with jerky or tense movements. Just prove this to yourself – try moving rhythmically with whatever you are doing and see how much less fatigued you feel. If you like you could imagine that music is playing and you are moving in time to the music, or hum a tune to yourself, or just get into the rhythm for that particular task – it will reveal its own rhythm to you if you are receptive.

You can apply this principle to all those mundane tasks that make up a large proportion of daily life, and you will find they take on a whole new aspect. If you move rhythmically through any chore it becomes more joyful – just try it and I'm sure you will be amazed. For instance, I hate ironing, and usually only do it just before I'm going on holiday. But a little while ago I began to iron in a rhythmical, flowing movement, using my whole body not just my arm, and I felt so released from my dislike and resentment of the task; it was a revelation. I felt as though I was dancing! A friend of mine who is a teacher of the Alexander technique uses this principle with her music students, especially with those learning the piano. She says if you move your whole body with your arms you will be less tired and achieve a more pleasing result. Now, when I'm seated at my computer keyboard I frequently move my body from side to side in a swaying movement, and again it is releasing and joyful and stops my back aching as it used to do. I urge you to try it, because we are not designed to sit in static postures for hours at a time. I also apply rhythm to vacuuming my house, and have almost begun to enjoy it, for it ceases to feel like a chore and a bore. All of me is moving *with* the task, rather than part of me being against it, and it feels more fun; I am focusing on what my body is doing rather than on the uninspiring task. I feel a great sense of harmony, rather than the discordant feeling of resistance and resentment. This is the point. When we move rhythmically, we are actually dancing with the universe; we are in harmony with the stars. Or, at least we are in a state of harmony within ourselves, which is most important.

So with every movement, from mowing the lawn to playing golf, from dusting your home to washing the car, or from making love to cooking your supper, try to bring rhythm and flow into it. Sometimes it may mean that something takes longer to perform, but if it tires you less and gives you more joy then surely it is worth reorganising your timetable a little.

And don't forget to walk rhythmically through your day. Usually we rush along with our behinds stuck out and our heads pushed forwards, hopelessly off-balance. Stand up straight and glide along, and see how much better it feels. It certainly looks better, and clothes look so much better on someone who moves gracefully and rhythmically – this applies to men as well as women. One of the wise Eastern sages wrote:

> *'When he walks, a wise man only walks.'*

In other words, just have your mind on the action of walking, when you are walking. Avoid thinking about anything else. It can be a kind of walking meditation. Try it, and experience how calming this can be.

It is a problem with today's world that we always have our mind's eye on the end result – the goal – rather than on the enjoyment of the action that takes you there. So many of my clients tell me that they are always rushing to get things finished. When I ask them what they are going to do after they've finished, they never really know. I say, 'What are you rushing to get to?' and usually they say, 'Nothing! Just to get everything completed.' But, of course, life is never completed until we are dead! And, sadly, we can miss out on so much enjoyment along the way. Some people seem to miss most of their life. How often have you heard someone say, 'Where have the last few years gone to?' You may have said it yourself.

Confucius apparently maintained that our goal in all endeavours in life should be harmony. Following this dictum, many Japanese businessmen try to organise their businesses and their transactions on this principle: the principle of prioritising the achievement of harmony above other considerations. Westerners trying to push through business deals rapidly, expediently, with the jerky timing of our rushed, speedy civilisation are often frustrated and bemused when things seem to take so long. They do not understand they are being eased gently into the principle of harmony, rhythm and timing. We can learn so much from other cultures.

Another point about moving rhythmically is that it makes everything seem more fun. Life so often feels like a constraint, a constriction, due to the lack of rhythm and flow in what we do. When we are out of sync, rushed and frantic, we work against ourselves, against our inner natural law of rhythm. I think we actually cause upset in our cells when we are discordant and inharmonious. But also we feel strained, and so cannot enjoy – we lose our connection to fun.

In her book, *The Continuum Concept*, author Jean Liedloff talks about her experience in a South American jungle, living for months at a time, during two and a half years, with a number of tribes of

Venezuelan Indians. She noted interesting aspects of their culture and ways of interacting with each other and, in particular, the rhythmical, natural continuum in the upbringing of their children. One description, however, that has always remained in my memory was her account of a group of five Indians, herself and two Italian men transporting a huge, heavy canoe over half a mile of boulders, which meant placing logs across the path of the canoe and hauling it, inch by inch, in the merciless sun. Inevitably, they slipped between the boulders on numerous occasions, scraping shins, ankles and whatever else landed against the granite. Several times the canoe would swing sideways, pinning one of them to the burning rock, until the others could move it off, and soon all ankles were bleeding! At one point, the author climbed onto a high rock to give herself a break with the pretext of taking photographs. From this higher vantage point she became aware of the sharp contrast in the way the Indians went about this strenuous task and the approach of their 'civilised' helpers. She noticed that the two Italian men were tense (as she had been), frowning, losing their tempers at everything and swearing non-stop 'in the distinctive manner of the Tuscan'. The Indians, however, were having a fine time. They were laughing at the unwieldiness of the canoe, making a game of the battle; they relaxed between pushes, laughing at their own scrapes and were especially amused when the canoe pinned one, then another, under-neath it. 'The fellow held bare-backed against the scorching granite, when he could breathe again, invariably laughed the loudest, enjoying his relief.' All were doing the same work; all were experiencing strain and pain. The only difference was in their attitudes towards what was happening to them. The Indians were revelling in the camaraderie, and each forward move was for them a little victory. In addition, they had had no build-up of dread of the task in the preceding days, as the others had. They were, consequently, less drained and more full of energy. There was no focus on the end result, of having to arrive back at the village within a certain timescale – no time urgency or deadline. The task and just being alive were the same. She said she experienced a wonderful rhythm in all the activities they engaged in; that the most remarkable thing was that they were never tired by their 'work'. For these wise Indians everything was equal. Nothing had more intensity than anything else – all of life was important and fun. There was no urgency – just enjoyment. They were joyful. It reminds me of the way children might go about an activity, and children do not tire in the way that adults do because they are joyful so much more of the time than adults.

Rhythm, of course, has different timescales to it. Think of the rhythms of nature; for example, the rhythm of the year. In this also are contained some lessons about living. There is a time for things to become dormant in the winter, and then there is a time of plenty in the spring, when life bursts forth in great abundance. The earth does not perform to just one, monotonous rhythm: it ups and lowers the tempo in the changing seasons. It can be helpful to bear the yearly rhythm in mind when we are becoming stressed and constricted, and realise that things take their time – we cannot always hurry and rush things along. So much of the time we want something to be accomplished in too short a space of time; we are beginning to measure productivity in milliseconds! But some things take longer than others and, if you consider the rhythm inherent in the yearly cycle, you may get a different perspective.

So, when you are getting in a state because something isn't being done fast enough, just stand back and say to yourself that everything has its own timing. Not everything takes the same amount of time and we are often tyrannised by deadlines or timetables that are unrealistic and have not been thought through in a creative way. Timing is very important in so many life areas and if we get it right so much else falls into place. Forcing things out of their own true rhythm never really works – think of artificially forced flowers, they never last as long as natural ones, and their blooms never look quite so beautiful.

Why rush?

One of the symptoms of stress is something called 'hurry sickness': the feeling that there is never enough time, of always being in a hurry, no matter what. This can become a bad habit, limiting our enjoyment of life. This attitude takes no account of differing rhythms and right timing. Someone who is always rushing is constantly in the future, never in the present. What is this driven attitude really saying? I think it is connected to what I have been talking about previously: it is the rush to get to some place of fulfilment after we have got everything 'done'. But that place is actually here now – why should it be sometime else? It is not a question of getting everything out of the way and *then* we can enjoy. Now can be the most sublime moment. It is the only moment we truly have, but so often we are not really living in the actual, present moment – we are thinking about yesterday or rushing towards tomorrow. But yesterday is gone forever and the next moment has not yet arrived. You can never live in the next moment – you always have to live in this moment. And we can make this 'now' moment exquisite, like the Indians do, if we are in it. Tomorrow, or later, is just a fantasy. And, anyway, when we get there – when it becomes now – we won't be there, we'll be rushing on.

Absolutely everything in the universe has its own rhythm. The more in tune we are with ourselves, the more we'll be in tune with others and with everything else around us. There is a time to ebb and a time to flow, a time to stop, let go and let it be, a time to rest, and a time to produce and do.

Also, consider the rhythm of day and night. Ask the Finnish and Icelandic people what it feels like to have sun for twenty-four hours, or darkness continuously round the clock. It is not conducive to wellbeing. The rhythm of light and dark seems to be something we also need. I think it is very important not to ignore this funda-mental phenomenon in nature – this phenomenon of rhythm – but to heed, and understand, its workings in ourselves, as well as in our daily schedules.

Be on holiday all the time

So, returning to the title of this chapter: it's not what you do it's the way that you do it. Think about how differently we do things in different contexts. For instance, think how you feel, and how you behave, when you are on holiday. Our inner attitude is usually completely different when away from home and/or work. So what has changed? We are still the same people but we tend to approach all that confronts us in a new way – we 'do' life differently. In that different context we develop a different mind-set. Where did it come from? And why leave it behind when we return home? Part of the answer, of course, is that we are more relaxed on holiday. But why not be relaxed all the time? Why not behave as if the whole of life is a holiday?

Think about how your body feels when you are away from work and home pressures – it flows, doesn't it. All your movements are more relaxed, and therefore more rhythmical. Think about your physical gestures when on holiday. You probably hold your body differently, with shoulders dropped, arms and hands relaxed, your breathing is probably slower and lower down in your abdomen. You probably smile many more times a day. You probably even laugh more. All of this adds up to a happier, healthier human being, but why only behave this way when distanced from the usual routine, and for only two weeks of the year?

I want to suggest that you hold on to that 'holiday feeling' when you get home again. Don't automatically tense up and start to rush. Keep the feeling of having a 'holiday body'. Keep your body loose and rhythmical; feel in harmony with your body. (Look in Chapter 7 for loosening exercises and much more on how to keep your body relaxed and free of tension.)

Try to see work and play as equal; think of work as being play and play as being important work, like the Venezuelan Indians I have mentioned above. I remember Picasso's daughter, Paloma, once saying that her father was always playing; that play was very important to him, in fact it was work to him and vice versa.

Call up in your imagination your attitude of mind when dealing with some problem during your holiday; try to bring that attitude back for everyday use.

I often cheer myself up by taking the attitude towards my day that I am actually on holiday. It really works – it lightens my step, lifts my mood and dispels that feeling of dread and anxiety about all that has to be done. So as you walk to the tube or bus look at your surroundings with new interest, pretend that this is a holiday resort and you are excited about it. Look at the people you pass with interest, trying to understand their way of life, as you would in a foreign country. Look at the beauty around you: the sky, the trees or the flowers in someone's front garden. Feel the pleasure of anticipation about what the day might hold, the exciting things that might occur. If we could try to approach our everyday activity with this attitude, wouldn't it be uplifting and wouldn't more people be a joy to interact with? We are talking about enthusiasm and the more enthusiasm you can muster, the more joy you will derive from all of your life – not just your short holiday time. We just have to take a little more control, not in a tense, control-freak kind of way, but in a relaxed and joyful way that is committed to 'doing it' differently.

Attitude, attitude, attitude

A certain prime minister recently said the three most important considerations for him were, 'Education, education, education,' and I would say that three of the most vital components in releasing oneself from stress and in attaining more joy, are, 'Attitude, attitude, attitude'. Attitude is most definitely another part of the *how*. Have you noticed how the most successful people generally have a delightful attitude – a positive, upbeat attitude? Just consider the way in which athletes, for example, talk about their performances – always with this positive, 'can-do' approach. That is what makes them winners. When we are on holiday we tend to have more of this type of attitude; if we can do it then, we have the potential to do it always! The following anonymous poem sums it up:

If you think you are beaten, you are
If you think you dare not, you don't
If you'd like to win, but think you can't
It's almost certain you won't.
If you think you'll lose, you've lost
For out of the world we find
Success begins with a fellow's will –
It's all in the state of mind.
If you think you're outclassed, you are
You've got to think high to rise
You've got to be sure of yourself before
You can ever win a prize.
Life's battles don't always go
To the stronger or faster man
But sooner or later the man who wins
Is the one who thinks he can.

One of the benefits of keeping our attitude positive, is that it just makes life feel easier; if it feels easier, then it will be – even if it isn't, if you see what I mean! We often stress ourselves by thinking negatively about whatever is facing us: seeing it as a trap, or an enemy that is out to get us, harm us, bring us down. But something is only what we *think* it is; if we don't think it is a problem, then it won't be, so it is really very important to work at this. If we can work to turn our attitudes around, and hold on to that holiday attitude and that holiday body feeling, we can release ourselves from a great deal of stress. I am not saying that nothing is a problem, and I don't wish to diminish true difficulties and stresses; but even when the outer situation is very difficult, if we can adjust our attitude to one of positivity in the face of the difficulty, we reduce our internal stress. Negativity is very disempowering, it saps your energy.

I remember hearing a well-known explorer talking on a radio programme about a recent expedition to the Arctic, and one of the things he said about survival struck me deeply as a guiding principle for everyday life. He said, 'You must develop the attitude of mind of making the snow and ice your friend and not your enemy.' He knew the importance of inner attitude for a successful outcome, and in those extreme conditions the help from inside yourself, in the absence of other sources, is vital.

So, whatever you have to deal with – be it the traffic jam, an incessant telephone, questions from your kids, colleagues to whom you have to give a presentation, a TV interview or a report to write – if you could make it your friend instead of your enemy, you would relax, feel harmonious and use less effort in dealing with it. Think about how your body posture changes if you are about to greet a friend. You anticipate pleasure and ease, so you relax and open yourself up to fun and enjoyment. Try to see the tasks of the day as friends and fun.

In the Arctic they know that disciplining themselves to adopt the right attitude is essential for their survival. But this also applies in, so-called, ordinary life. We will all survive and succeed better with a positive attitude and approach, as well as with an enhanced sense of rhythm, harmony and fun. And in the following chapter I give you a specific technique to assist you in all of this.

10

The power of 'Yes'

Following on from the previous chapter, I should like to tell you of a technique I teach my clients, which has very positive results. I usually introduce it when people tell me they are feeling negative, fearful, overloaded, anxious about their abilities or just unmotivated.

To get round the blocks we sometimes feel within ourselves, which prevent us from functioning well, or at all, I suggest to my clients that they link into the power of repeating 'Yes!' Just saying it over and over in your mind, or out loud, will have a very tangible effect on your state of body and mind. Yes is positive and powerful. It is such a simple little word but it can change your inner state. The words we use to ourselves inwardly are of paramount importance, for they are taken into our unconscious mind and believed. The unconscious does not discriminate about the information it receives: it believes everything you tell it, rather like a child; it does not reason. So if you give yourself negative messages, then that is the belief system you are programming into your unconscious. This negativity will then become manifest in your life. But you can, with a little sustained effort, create a positive and powerful programme that will uplift you, clear away the blocks and help you in daily living. This will help you to achieve what the previous chapter has been discussing.

When you catch yourself saying 'No' to something you don't want to do, but have to do, turn it around and say 'Yes, I am going to do that. Yes! Yes! Yes! I want to. Yes!' And experience what a huge difference it makes to how you feel. It changes the vibrations in your physical body; the vibrations in your cells. 'Yes' causes you to embrace rather than reject. If you are pulling back from something that has to be faced, then this is the way to help yourself. Keep saying 'Yes! Yes!', and you will feel your energy changing – you'll vibrate with power! Just experience it.

So switch on the power with 'Yes!' Instead of pulling back, push forward by encouraging yourself from within with this positive word. Very often the thought of 'No' causes tension. And tension in our muscles is usually a physical expression of a mental 'No'; of resistance of some sort. When we say 'Yes' we relax, we open up: we affirm, accept and let go. 'Yes' is a form of 'amen', which means 'so be it'. It is an acceptance of what is. But more than that, it pushes us forwards; it expels our breath out into the world. It pushes us more into the world. 'No' makes us retreat. 'No' is withdrawal; it pulls back. 'Yes' goes forwards.

Just say those two little words a number of times, and experience the body feeling. The body responds to what the mind tells it. Say 'No' and feel the shrinking feeling inside. Say it again and experience the denial, the putting up of a barrier. Now say 'Yes' and feel the difference. Feel the expansion, the opening up, the lightness of it. Say it again and again. Keep experiencing the difference in your state: in both your physical body and your mind. Feel how 'Yes' puts your mouth into a smile.

So, whenever you are experiencing any kind of difficulty, just say 'Yes!' to yourself. Keep repeating that little word: 'Yes! Yes! Yes!' It may not seem logical or make any rational sense in the context of your problem, but just keep saying it nonetheless. More and more you will feel a difference in your thoughts and feelings. Things will open up. You will lighten up. You will tingle with the positive vibration. You will feel the positive power it bestows.

Overcoming panic with 'Yes'

One client of mine was having great difficulty leaving home in the mornings to travel to work. She experienced frequent panic attacks and extreme anxiety and was frightened to go far from home in case she 'lost control'. I worked with her on this problem by teaching her how to relax all through her body before leaving the house, as well as going through a very simple exercise routine to loosen her muscles and to get her circulation flowing well. She then used the above technique. She just said to herself that, yes, she wanted to go to work, and yes, she was going to work, and yes, she was going to walk to the bus stop. So, in spite of her automatic reaction to resist going out, she simply over-rode it with a positive message. It was hard at first, because she did not believe the 'Yes' message, but she kept working with it, encouraging herself to go with the 'Yes' and not with the 'No', and eventually the fear and panic receded. She began to recognise that she was capable of travelling to work without anything 'terrible' happening to her, and her confidence in herself grew – her sense of her own power to overcome her inner fears also grew.

Becoming positive

Often when we say 'No' to whatever is facing us, it is because we don't believe in ourselves or in our own ability. By using the positivity of 'Yes!' we can overcome our insecurities and inner doubts. It is simply in refusing to be held back that we weaken the power of the negative. In refusing to listen to the internal words of doubt, and saying 'Yes! I am going to do it', you resist being controlled by the debilitating thoughts. When we give our attention to something we are also directing our power towards it, our energy. So we must be mindful of where we direct our attention. We can make a choice about whether or not to believe something, and that includes the thoughts that are presented to us by our minds. We can make a decision to choose what we want to think. And as what we think is presented in the form of words, then we have to be careful about the words we listen to. But we can change the words in our minds. We must become the director of our minds – the boss – not the subordinate.

The power of 'Yes!' is a very effective tool to carry around with you in your mental stress-release toolkit. Do not be fooled by the simplicity of this concept. It is indeed simple, but that does not detract from its power. It really works! Put it to the test. Just keep trying it out in your life and you will see how useful a tool it is. In fact, I love the simplicity of this thought. As the well-known advertisement says, 'Life's complicated enough!' The simpler we can make things the better we'll feel.

However, an extension of the power of 'Yes!' is to consider the power of all positive words. When we use them to encourage ourselves, or others, we create a powerful energy that we can use to our advantage. For example, a lot of internal stress is generated by our inner critic – we all have one! So, when you realise you are criticising yourself, try changing the words you are using, and start encouraging yourself internally with positive affirmations. Tell yourself what you are good at and what your successes have been. Build up a positive picture in your mind and you will find it creates a positive feeling. This works in a very practical way. Whatever we tell ourselves, we believe, as already discussed. So why tell ourselves negative, dreary, fearful things? As Shakespeare said, 'There is nothing right or wrong, but thinking makes it so.' It all starts in the mind.

Using your mind

Our mind uses words to inform us, most of the time (except in dreams and imaginings, when it uses pictures and images). And we use words to inform others of our thoughts or desires and so on. So, after you have worked on perfecting the power of 'Yes' (and have it firmly established in your internal stress-release toolkit), begin to concentrate more attentively on all the words you use. Find the right words and you can more easily release the stress in yourself and others. Keep reminding yourself of this fact – it's not what you say, it's the way that you say it *and* the words you use!

Different words have different strengths – but all words have some kind of power. The power to heal or the power to wound, the power to encourage or the power to deflate. It is important to be mindful of this both with the words we use to others, and with those we use to ourselves.

Practise saying certain words to yourself, or out loud when you are alone, and experience their power. Practice different ways of saying the same thing to someone. For example, if you have to give some bad news to a friend or colleague, experiment with the impact of phrasing it in a number of different ways. Or, if you know you have expressed something rather badly, or negatively, try out another way of communicating the same message, using words with a different energy. For, even if we have to give a negative message, it will be heard more effectively if we can present it with a positive power, rather than a negative or wounding power. Equally, when we are required to give bad news, or negative messages, we will shrink from it less if we've found a healing and positive expression for the delivery.

Focusing on the words you use is the best way to begin to take more control over your mind, which will affect your interaction with yourself as well as with others. Things generally work better in all kinds of situations when we use positive words. This is how we create a positive attitude. You are what you think. It is what you say it is.

11

How do we find fulfilment?

In my view, the greatest problem of today's world is a creeping cynicism, accompanied much of the time by what seems to me to verge on nihilism. I feel it is imperative that we rediscover childlike enthusiasm and wonder and that we find meaning in our lives. Many people tell me that life has very little meaning for them. This is not only sad, but worrying, because if we do not have a sense of meaning, then what is the point of anything? I firmly believe that we each have to find our own meaning. We need to find a personal reason to get up in the morning – no one is going to hand us 'meaning' on a plate. But if we have no vision, no dream, then we cannot fulfil ourselves.

I was struck by another of the pertinent observations Kevin Costner made in the TV interview I have already mentioned. He said, 'You should be about something, and not give it up because it is not in vogue. You must go for your dream and not be afraid to fail. When you lose your dreams you become ancient.' Again, I agree with him. We must not lose our dreams and our visions for the future. But I think we may be chasing the wrong dream and that is why it doesn't fulfil us. For, in my view, we are looking in the wrong place for happiness and fulfilment if we imagine they will be delivered by the consumer society, by the corporate world. I believe the greatest happiness and fulfilment arise from looking inside ourselves and connecting with our imagination and with our soul.

A quote I like says, 'Imagination is the eye of the soul.' When we have opened 'the eye of the soul' then we can bring forth the visions of our inner world to connect with the outer world. I believe it is in this interaction of inner and outer, this joining of the two worlds, that fulfilment and joy arise.

So many of today's aspirations only satisfy our egos and not our souls and this is why we cannot find meaning. The satisfaction doesn't go deep enough. It's like desert sand with nothing to root it down and hold it in place; it is easily blown away. It is the reason we feel so much discontentment – lost, adrift and unfulfilled. We need to aspire to *be* more within ourselves, not to *have* more: to be spiritually aspirational rather than materially so; to look inside and connect with our essence. That way we take back the control from the outside world and claim it for our inner self.

The Dalai Lama, in his book *The Art of Happiness*, says something very important on this subject. He is asked about the problem of having so many desires in the consumer society, and his answer is that it is natural to have desires, but we need to ask ourselves if the fulfilling of a particular desire will really make us happy. He states that certain things may give us pleasure for a while but that pleasure is usually only fleeting and does not lead to lasting happiness. He says that giving in to pleasure often makes us unhappy in the long term. According to Buddhist principles, happiness is the goal we should strive for, and that may mean we have to deny ourselves the fulfilment of pleasure. He gives the example of the pleasure of eating to excess or drinking too much or taking drugs. All of these things may give us the experience of immediate pleasure but once the effects have worn off the result may be a feeling of unhappiness at having overindulged. Suspending pleasure may lead to a happier state of being.

Lasting fulfilment does not come from momentary pleasure, or unsustainable thrills and highs. For example, the instant pleasure of buying a new piece of clothing can give us a lift for a while because it renews our view of ourselves; it changes the way we see ourselves and, we hope, the way the world sees us. A new look implies a new personality – but it is transitory and the thrill quickly wears off. But in my view this is not the whole story: it is not totally superficial. For what we are encountering in our new outer look is a glimpse of the potential inside ourselves. Equally, what may be glimpsed through alcohol or some drugs may also be pointing to the riches locked up inside, riches that we have not yet tapped. That is what we are really after: the *more* that is inside; the deeper transformation or the metamorphosis into our true self.

Fulfilment comes from connecting with your deeper self and listening to your inner voice. One of the gateways to this connection, and thus greater fulfilment, is to tap your creativity and relate more to the artist in yourself.

Connecting to your creativity

When we express ourselves artistically and creatively, a deeper experience is achieved. Producing something from within yourself reveals you to yourself – it expresses the uniqueness that is you and nobody else. So when we produce creatively, we see ourselves more clearly and this is incredibly reassuring and affirming. We also experience our power to make a difference. When we are creative something from our inner world moves into the outer world: the opposite flow to consuming. So by manifesting something that was not there before, we experience our power to change the world by our artistic efforts.

But perhaps most importantly, in any act of creation we glimpse the treasures and richness of our imagination – the abundance within. There is an incredible landscape within us, a boundless internal universe, which when tapped into can transport us to sublime heights of happiness, bliss and even ecstasy. An experience far greater and infinitely more satisfying and lasting than anything the outer world can induce. Our imaginations are like inner adventure playgrounds containing limitless possibilities; we need to travel more frequently inside ourselves, to go on an adventure into the interior: there is so much to explore. Once you start working with your imagination, it really is very exciting. You never quite know what will come up next. It is definitely the opposite of boring. Many young people today complain of being easily bored, which I believe is a result of absorbing too much of other people's creativity and not having sufficient opportunity to experience their own. I can guarantee any boredom will vanish if you get into some sort of imaginative and creative activity. This is largely because you will be experiencing *yourself* in a fresh way, and actually using the storehouse of treasures within you.

We need to see ourselves in our totality – we are so much! We need to see ourselves as minds, imaginations, hearts, souls, beautiful beings. And we have to use ourselves – our real selves. Most of us don't use a fraction of our potential.

So try to connect with the artist in yourself. Remember what you enjoyed doing as a child, for as children we so often loved to paint or draw, sing or play a musical instrument (however badly!), to make up rhymes, write poetry or adventure stories, dance, dress up and act at being other characters. We constantly used our imaginations and our creativity. We need to get using them again. We badly need to keep alive the artistic side of our natures. Artistic expression connects us to our souls because the soul is within, not in the outside world. And the beauty of artistic expression is nourishment to the soul.

Try to fit some kind of imaginative and artistic expression into your agenda at least once a week, but preferably more often. It is not important how 'good' you are, that is not the point. It is about the process of creation more than the result; it is the doing of it that gives you the experience – the joy, the fulfilment. Perhaps take up something you used to enjoy but which got squeezed out of your life by all the practical and mundane duties; reclaim that part of your life – that part of you. Go to painting classes, join a dance class, learn (or re-learn) a musical instrument, find a singing teacher, join a choir or your local amateur dramatic society, take up dressmaking or embroidery, flower arranging, gardening, pottery, sculpture, photography or creative writing. There are so many wonderful artistic activities to enjoy and I'm sure you can think of many I have left out. They create a balance with the dry, serious, logical intellect that most of us overuse. The imaginative use of your brain moves you from the left to the right hemisphere; this refreshes and enlivens. It truly strengthens your life-forces when you engage in artistic and creative endeavours, which, of course, has a beneficial effect on your whole being. It is vital not to allow this side of yourself to become dead.

In addition, try to live your whole life as an 'art form'. This means trying to do everything artistically – whether it is having a conversation or telling someone off, it can be done with artistry. Make sure your environment is artistic: fill it with beautiful flowers, introduce uplifting or soothing scents with incense sticks or essential oil burners, pay attention to the lighting, have your favourite colours around you, and play music appropriate to the mood you want to create whenever you can. Organise your timetable artistically: balance the activities in which you engage, so that the mundane are interspersed with the creative, uplifting ones. However, you will find that if you try to do everything artistically even the mundane activities will seem less of a chore.

Even if you have very little time for artistic expression, at least you could sing in the shower! Also, sing in the car, instead of fuming at other drivers! It will uplift you, and is a great way to release your tightly held breath. Singing automatically takes the breathing down to the diaphragm, as well as moving you from your left brain into your right, creative brain. Sing with your children (it is actually a very good remedy for car sickness) or recite poems on car journeys or make up stories or encourage them to tell you imaginative stories; do the same with your partner or friends. If you start the ball rolling, the others will feel released into the artistic side of their natures.

A few more suggestions to get you started: place a sketching pad beside the telephone, so that you can use it whenever a small space opens up. Draw some shapes or pictures or 'doodles' as you sit talking on the phone or waiting to be connected. Perhaps also have a jar full of coloured pencils to add to the artistry (and fun!). It doesn't have to be of 'great master' standard – this is just to release you into your creative side. I have a large easel up in my kitchen with paper and crayons always available in case anyone wants to express themselves artistically at any time. There are many ways you can bring creativity into your world.

I think we should bring back the art of storytelling – we should have storytelling gatherings, with young and old together – it would really enhance community. Maybe start a storytelling group with your friends.

Dance whenever you can! Our bodies were designed to be in movement, not to sit still all day. Dance around your house, or put on uplifting music in the kitchen when you are cooking a meal and sing along, or dance to it. I am reminded of a wonderful scene in the film *Mermaids*, with Cher, as the mother, and her two on-screen daughters dancing and singing around their kitchen as they prepared supper. Why does it only happen in movies? It needn't. Actually, I often dance through cooking a meal, and it makes me laugh, which is enormously relaxing and releasing. I also put on my favourite music and dance to it late at night, or if there is a programme about music on TV, I get up off my sofa and dance along with it, to get my body moving. It speeds up the circulation and enlivens my whole being, and the world seems a better place.

We have to make it happen in our lives – not just watch it in the movies. No one is going to do it for us! We have to take responsibility for enlivening our lives and that means we have to enliven ourselves in the ways I have been discussing above. It will all lead to greater fulfilment and contentment and will engage so much more of you than just 'the shopper' or 'the PA' or 'the managing director' or whatever – you will connect to the deeper 'you'. Get together with friends and have fun. Whenever we enjoy ourselves and have fun, creativity will arise. For often, when we 'forget' ourselves – which means our superficial selves – we then move closer to our true selves. When we relax and let go we connect with our intuitive self. Just consider that word for a moment: intuition – what it actually signifies is the teacher within, or the inner wisdom which we all contain. Intuition, or inner wisdom, cannot be forced, it has to be allowed. And we allow it to enter consciousness by relaxing, letting go and opening up the channel to our creative self.

Meditation

Meditation is another way in which we connect to our inner self and can hear the inner voice. This also has a stabilising effect and brings a sense of quiet fulfilment. When we become inwardly quiet we experience a new dimension of ourselves. Sometimes people are afraid of being silent and doing 'nothing'; I think often they fear they will somehow disintegrate or fall apart. Actually the exact opposite is the case. With regular practice of meditation there is an increasing sense of profound integration: of everything coming together in unity and harmony. The more frequently you connect to the 'inner you' the greater will be your experience of a calm, centred certainty. It is a feeling that all is right with the world, and a sense that there is nothing to strive for – nothing to be frantically searching for. It is really all here right now, right this moment – only we are usually not looking. So much of the time we are looking into the future or back at the past – we are absent minded: our minds are elsewhere. How can we see the exquisite present if our minds are not here? Therefore, in addition to setting special time aside for meditation, try to bring your mind into the present moment as often as you can, for it truly offers the opportunity to experience timelessness and tranquility. We can never find tranquility if we keep thinking that what we need is somewhere else! One of my clients recently said (much to my joy), 'If you're constantly chasing something, it's never where you are.' She instinctively grasped this truth.

You will also feel restless if you think that what you need is always outside yourself. The most sublime and fulfilling experiences, I believe, happen as a result of first being connected with the 'inner' aspect of ourselves, then joining our inner world with something in the outer world as well. But if we have not first connected to our own creative, intuitive self, we shall not have sufficient to bring to the meeting. I think this is why some things feel bleak and unfulfil-ling, when we had expected them to make us happy or cheer us up, to provide enjoyment or uplift. It is because we are not properly 'wired up', as it were, to our side of the equation. If you meet the world, be it the world of entertainment or art, work or social life, or another human being, with an emptiness within – unconnected to your real self – then there is nothing for that other to react with. But when we bring our fullest self to the encounter with anything, or anyone else, that is when we experience magic! That is the mystical, sublime experience that is spoken of by poets, songwriters and lovers, and which we have all glimpsed – however fleetingly; it happens when we offer all that we truly are to whatever we meet with. Then you have the result of two and two becoming five – it is the experience of that 'extra something' being present.

I should like to add a final thought about fulfilment. I believe fulfilment is also to be found in altruistic activities. Helping others, or giving one's time and talents to a cause or organisation you believe in, is enormously rewarding in a multitude of ways. Again, this kind of activity shows you what you have to offer, who you are and how you can make a difference. It makes you feel valuable, and usually valued by others as well. It also connects you with something outside yourself in a meaningful way, and potentially opens up a two-way channel to love. So, if you feel moved to take up some charitable work in the evenings, or volunteer as a hospital helper or prison visitor or whatever it may be, act immediately on that altruistic impulse, for you will find one thing leads to another and a small step can ripple out to make a positive difference to every-body you are involved with. Any commitment to a higher ideal helps us to become more, to grow and to go on developing. In many ways you could say that it is in our ability to be idealistic, and to act from that standpoint, that we are being most human.

Commitment itself has a great power and once you truly make a commitment to something you will discover your energy and enthusiasm increasing, which usually imparts a greater sense of purpose or meaning. The famous quote from Goethe says it well:

> '. . . until one is committed there is hesitancy, the chance to draw
> back, always ineffectiveness, concerning all acts of initiative and
> creation. There is one elementary truth, the ignorance of which
> kills countless ideas and splendid plans: that the moment one
> definitely commits oneself then Providence moves too. All sorts of
> things occur to help one that would never otherwise have occur-
> red. A whole stream of events issues from the decision, raising in
> one's favour all manner of unforeseen incidents and meetings
> and material assistance which no man could have dreamed
> would have come his way.
>
> Whatever you can do, or dream you can, begin it.
> Boldness has genius, power and magic in it.
> Begin it now!'

This kind of commitment may also mean that you are doing
something completely in contrast to your usual daily activities,
which is in itself refreshing. Sometimes doing more, but of a
different nature to one's usual life, is not exhausting, as you might
imagine, but energising. That old maxim: 'A change is as good as a
rest' holds true here. Those so-called old wives' sayings contain a
great deal of wisdom.

Make a commitment to yourself.
To connecting with your inner self.
To using your creativity.
To discovering fulfilment through listening to your soul.

(You will be able to find names of volunteer organisations and
charities by contacting your local church, Citizen's Advice organisation, or by looking in the telephone directory.)

Afterword

I have presented you with my ideas and suggestions for releasing your stress – as well as the essential information – and I hope that I have shown you how to take a different view sometimes; how to change the perspective and think about things another way. This is the major key to your release: to recognise that we always have choices. Everything can be experienced from a number of different standpoints and we can choose the most useful view at any time; the most helpful way for us to see things at that moment. Just because we have always seen something in one way it doesn't mean there is no other way to see it, or that we have to continue seeing it as we always have done. When you search for an alternative approach to some problem or difficulty that is when you begin to free yourself, because you increase your options. Always ask yourself, 'Is there another way I could be looking at this?' This is how we can move forwards and transform things for the better.

Most importantly, however, please remember that all the suggestions contained in these pages need to be worked at every day, and that it takes time to bring about changes in ourselves and our outlook. Be gentle with yourself and patient. If one day it isn't working and you feel downhearted or overwhelmed just reassure yourself, encourage yourself, that tomorrow it can all be different.

Each day is a new opportunity to get it right, to make it more beautiful, to do 'it' differently. I often think the days of our lives are like the weather, ever changing. Just because today is stormy, or dull and heavy, it doesn't mean tomorrow will be exactly the same. The bad times roll away like dark clouds and suddenly, unexpectedly, the sun bursts through. So never despair. Especially, never forget the important point that the sun is always there, it doesn't disappear – it only seems to. It gets covered up, or escapes our gaze for a while, but it still exists somewhere. This is what happens to all the good things in life. They are always there, waiting for us to find our way back to them. This book is a 'way' – a way back to what you long for, to what you know is true.

> *'Go placidly amid the noise and haste . . .'*

I wish you joy, fulfilment and happiness, but above all, love.

The Susan Balfour relaxation audio cassette and CD

My audio cassette and CD of loosening and unwinding exercises, calm breathing technique and deep relaxation will enable you to be more in control of your reactions to the stresses and pressures in your life. For while we cannot control many of the outer events that occur to try us, we can control the effect they have on us. Life and other people wind us up, but nobody unwinds us – we have to do that for ourselves! And that is why I have produced this audio cassette and CD. All the gentle movements and techniques are a practical help and support for coping with the stresses of everyday living. They should be used whenever you feel you are becoming tense and tight, or when you feel overwhelmed by the problems or demands of your life. The more often you listen to these relaxing techniques, the more it will become automatic for you to switch on the 'relaxation response' instead of the 'stress response'.

To order copies of the above please contact:

Susan Balfour
c/o Pasha Universal Ltd.,
Suite 243
405 King's Road
London SW10 0BB
UK

Telephone: 020 7736 4922

Suggested further reading

Chopra, Deepak, *Ageless Body, Timeless Mind*, Rider, 1993

Covey, Stephen R., *The Seven Habits of Highly Effective People*, Simon & Schuster, 1992

Dalai Lama and Norman, Alexander, *Ancient Wisdom, Modern World: Ethics for the New Millennium*, Abacus, 2000.

Dalai Lama and Cutler, Howard C., *The Art of Happiness*, Hodder & Stoughton, 1998

Dalai Lama, *The Power of Compassion*, Thorsons, 1995

Diamond, Harvey and Diamond, Marilyn, *Fit for Life*, Bantam, 1995

Frankl, Viktor, *Man's Search for Meaning*, Hodder & Stoughton, 1997

Fromm, Erich, *The Art of Loving*, Thorsons, 1995

Gelb, Michael, *Body Learning: An Introduction to the Alexander Technique*, revised edition, Aurum Press, 1994

Goleman, Daniel, *Emotional Intelligence*, Bloomsbury, 1996

Grant, Doris, *Food Combining for Life*, Thorsons, 1995

Hay, Louise, *Life! Reflections on Your Journey*, Hay House, 1995

Hendrix, Harville, *Getting the Love You Want*, HarperCollins, 1990

Jeffers, Susan, *End the Struggle and Dance with Life*, Hodder & Stoughton, 1996

Jeffers, Susan, *Feel the Fear and Do It Anyway*, Arrow, 1991

Peck, M. Scott, *The Road Less Travelled*, Arrow, 1990

Rowe, Dorothy, *Depression: The Way Out of Your Prison*, second edition, Routledge, 1996

Tissier, Jackie le, *Food Combining for Vegetarians*, Thorsons, 1992

Trickett, Shirley, *Coping Successfully with Panic Attacks*, Sheldon Press, 1998

Weekes, Claire, *Self Help for Your Nerves*, Thorsons, 1995

Recommended 'Little' Books

Dalai Lama, *The Little Book of Wisdom*, Rider, 1997

Emerson, Ralph Waldo, *Friendship*, Souvenir Press, 1999

Gibran, Kahlil, *The Prophet*, Heinemann, 1993

Jeffers, Susan, *The Little Book of Peace*, Hodder & Stoughton, 2001

Pas, Julian F., *The Wisdom of the Tao*, Oneworld Publications, 2000

Schiller, David, *The Little Zen Companion*, Workman Publishing, 1994

White Eagle, *The Quiet Mind*, The White Eagle Publishing Trust, 1998

Wilson, Paul, *The Little Book of Calm*, Penguin Books, 1997

Wilson, Paul, *The Little Book of Hope*, Penguin Books, 1999

Index